ERICA LARKCOM
KATHY EVANS
ROGER DELPECH
Editor: John Gogarty

Edexcel International GCSE Biology

EDEXCEL CERTIFICATE IN BIOLOGY

PRACTICE BO

Acknowledgments

The publisher would like to thank the following for permission to reproduce copyright material:

p.26 data for graph bottom right from 'A novel approach to photosynthesis practicals' Debbie Eldridge, *School Science Review*, **85** (312) (2004) The Association for Science Education; **p.27** Graph 1 & 2 from *Vital Signs 2001 to 2002*, Worldwatch Institute, Earthscan Publications; **p.46** data adapted from www.comprehensivephysiology.com/WileyCDA/CompPhysArticle/refldcp040110.htm; **p.47** data on water balance in a kangaroo rat from *Animal Physiology*, Knut Schmidt-Nielsen (1979) Cambridge University Press and *Desert Animals*, (1979) Dover Publications; **p.47** graph from http://apps.cmsfq.edu.ec/biologyexploringlife/text/chapter32/review32.html; **p.58** top diagram from *London Examinations 1557/09 Science: Double Award (Modular GASP)* (1997) Qu 7; **p.58** headline taken from a report by England's Chief Medical Officer (2013); **p.62** Graph A from http://www.esrl.noaa.gov/gmd/ccgg/trends/weekly.html; **p.63** Graph B from http://www.esrl.noaa.gov/gmd/ccgg/trends; **p.63** data for table from *Plants for primary pupils 5. Plants in their natural environment*, pp29–30, (2009) Science and Plants for Schools/Field Studies Council; **p.67** data from Robin Sutton, Field Studies Council, personal communication; **p.68** food web from http://mdk12.org/instruction/clg/public_release/biology/G3_E5_I3.html; **p.70** lichen map of England and Wales from www.britishlichensociety.org.uk; **p.73** data for graph from *School Science Review,* **76** (274) (1994) Hewitson and Price; **p.75** data from *Postharvest technology of fruit and vegetables,* p89, Thompson AK (1996) Blackwell Science Ltd; **p.76** aquaculture data from *Fisheries and Aquaculture Statistics*; **p.78** data courtesy of Longs Farm, Heartest; **p.79** diagram from *Science and Plants for Schools* and *Kew*.

Photo credit: **p.29** © Roger Delpech.

Orders: please contact Bookpoint Ltd, 130 Milton Park, Abingdon, Oxon OX14 4SB.
Telephone: (44) 01235 827720. Fax: (44) 01235 400454. Lines are open 9.00–17.00, Monday to Saturday, with a 24-hour message answering service. Visit our website at www.hoddereducation.co.uk

First published in 2013 by

Hodder Education

An Hachette UK Company,

338 Euston Road

London NW1 3BH

Impression number	5	4	3	2	1
Year	2017	2016	2015	2014	2013

Cover photo © Stuart Monk - Fotolia

Typeset in ITC Legacy Serif by Aptara Inc.

Printed in Spain

A catalogue record for this title is available from the British Library

ISBN 978 1 444 179187

Contents

Get the most from this book

This Practice Book will help you to prepare for your International GCSE Biology assessment. The questions are arranged in Sections that closely match the content of the Specification, so that you can use this book throughout the year as you study each Section and as part of your final revision.

Within these Sections, we have included lots of examples of different types of questions that may be used in your IGCSE Biology examinations. For each question type, you will find a sample question and two different student responses with comments that help you understand how to approach the question. Always look at the mark allocation to guide you in your answer.

Questions given under the title **Practical activities** include questions that test your understanding and experience of practical skills. Many of these questions link directly with experiments and investigations listed in the specification and you should make sure you can answer them even if you have not done the experiment or investigation yourself.

Questions given under the title **Using and interpreting data** include plotting graphs and interpreting data, both numerical and descriptive, but are related closely to familiar topics in the specification. **Applying principles** questions ask you to apply your biological understanding to unfamiliar situations, within the context of topics studied in the specification.

Remember, in your final examination, a single question may cover material from more than one part of the specification and a similar approach is adopted in many of the questions in this book. For a thorough understanding of biology it is important to make connections between topics in different sections. Make sure you revise well and cover all the questions in this book.

All answers are available online at www.hodderplus.co.uk/edexcelgcsescience

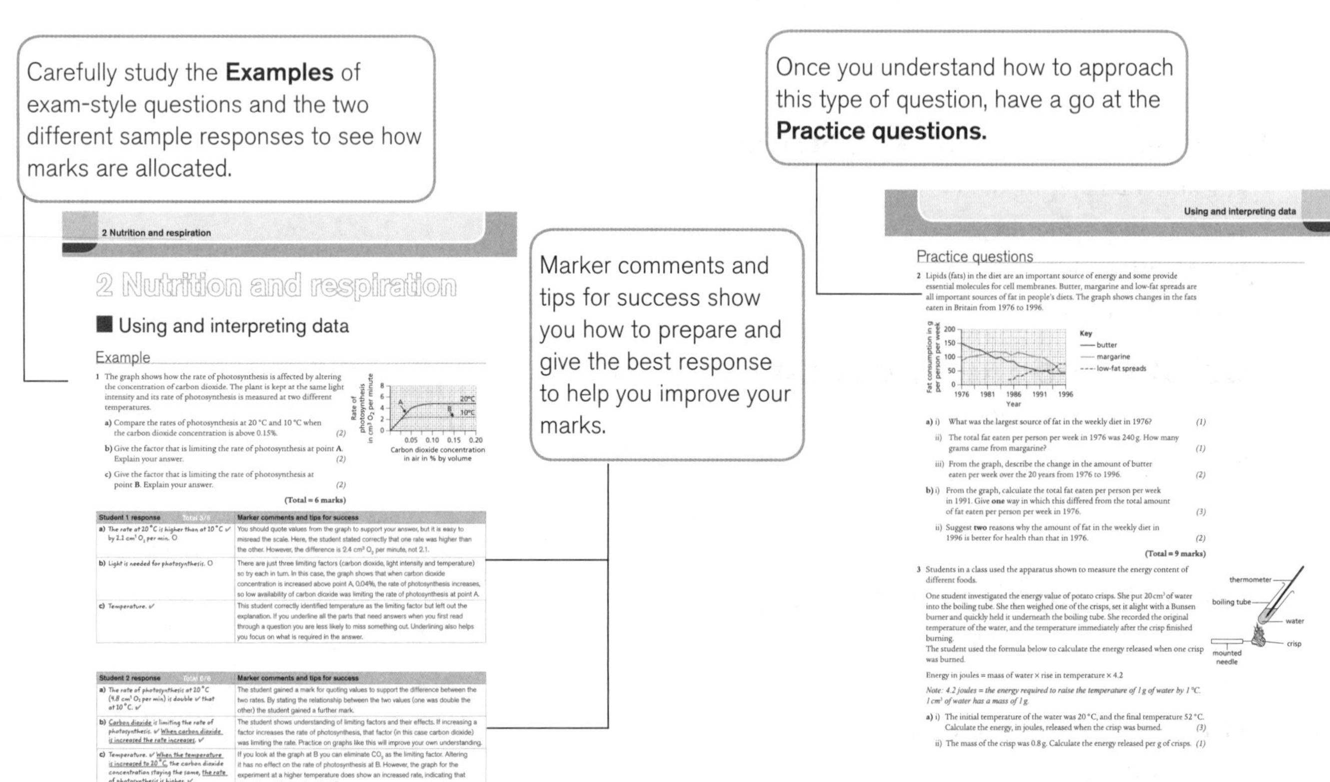

Examination advice

1 Always look at the mark allocation for the question part. For example, if the questions is out of (3) marks it's no good writing one word. You need to make 3 separate points to gain 3 marks.

An exception to this is for calculations. If you show no working but do get the right answer, usually you gain full marks. But you are always advised to show the steps in your working in case you have made a mistake. You may, for example, have read the correct figures from a graph but done an incorrect calculation or you may have misread the figures but used the correct method for the calculation. In each case, you would get some of the marks for the steps in the working you have shown.

2 The mark allocation also gives an indication of the time you might spend on that question part. Often '1 mark a minute' is a useful guide, but check the total number of marks in the paper and the time allowed. Then work out the time you can spend on each question (before you make a start) to make sure you make a sensible attempt at all the questions. It is usually easy to get the first few marks but harder to get the last marks – so use your time sensibly.

3 Look carefully at the 'prompt' words in the question.

Word used in the question	Explanation and ways to approach the question
Describe	Usually requires a concise and straightforward factual account of the event, process or perhaps data and trends, presented in a graph or table
Explain	Requires some sort of reason behind the description and expects you to draw on other biological knowledge, usually earns 2 or more marks
Suggest	Implies that you draw on material that you have not learnt directly in your specification, but is sensible in the context, using your biological knowledge
Advantages and disadvantages or Comparisons / differences between	Requires you to say something about both aspects. You are unlikely to get full marks if you refer to only one

4 Spelling does matter, particularly when you are referring to biological terms. Sometimes incorrect spelling means something else (e.g. ureter, urethra, uterus).

5 Read the question ONCE, TWICE and even THREE times to make sure you have understood exactly what the question is asking. Make sure you give an answer to the question set (and not what you might have preferred it to be). Then leave yourself enough time to check your answers at the end of the examination.

6 In your real examination paper, the number of lines helps to give you an idea of how much to write. In this Practice Book, you should look carefully at the mark allocation as a guide.

7 Be careful when drawing graphs. In the student responses and commentaries there are various instructions for how to tackle graphs. In Biology, for line graphs, you are always advised to join the points with straight lines, from one point to the next (but make sure the position of the points remain clear).

Using the mark schemes

Examiners use the mark schemes to guide them when they do the marking. The mark schemes say precisely what is correct or accepted as an answer (and often what is not accepted). They show how many marks to give for each part of each question.

In this book, we include mark schemes that are very similar in style to those used by examiners. Some mark schemes (for some Extended writing questions and one CORMS question) are printed in the Practice book, and mark schemes for all the questions are available for you online at www.hodderplus.co.uk/edexcelgcsescience

The table below gives you some of the shorthand symbols we use in the book and the online mark schemes, and other helpful notes about the mark schemes.

Dot (•) at the start of the line	Each point in the mark scheme starts on a separate line, shown by a dot (•) at the start of the line.
Oblique (/)	Often there are different possible answers, any of which is acceptable, so these alternative answers are separated by an oblique (/). Sometimes there is only one word (or group of words) that is acceptable for an answer, so this word must be given to gain the mark.
'eq'	'eq' stands for 'equivalent' – there could be other ways of phrasing the answer (provided it is close to the word given) or there may be other suitable examples (but only a few are listed).
More mark descriptions than the total	Sometimes there are more mark descriptions than the total for that part of the question. There could, for example, be a list of six marking points but only 4 marks for the question part. The maximum marks awarded would be 4, but you can see that there is some flexibility as to how you achieve those marks. Even if you give six points that are all correct, you can score only a maximum of 4 marks.
'Internal maximum'	In certain questions – e.g. when making comparisons between two features – there may be an 'internal maximum' showing how you must refer to both features to gain full marks. You cannot just write all your answer about one feature and expect to gain full marks.
Words in (brackets)	Some words are given in brackets – this means that the words need not be repeated in giving the information for the marking point, but the context or reference must be clear. Sometimes these words may have been given credit earlier in an answer.
Words in italics	Words in italics generally give further explanations or other examples that could be used.
Show your working in calculations	In calculations you are always advised to show the steps in your working. This may, for example, show that you have read off two figures correctly from a graph but made a mistake in doing the rest of the calculation so that the answer is incorrect. In this case, you would get some marks for the correct readings but not for the final answer. If, however, you show no working but do get the correct answer, usually you get the full marks.
'Example'	'Example' indicates that you can give further support to your answer (and gain more marks) by referring to a relevant example that helps illustrate the point.
Marks for each part	The marks for each part are shown in a separate column. You cannot 'transfer' marks and get a mark for saying something (even though it is correct) in a different part of the question.

1 Living organisms: variety and common features

Using and interpreting data

Example

1 Catalase is an enzyme found in many plant and animal cells. It catalyses the breakdown of hydrogen peroxide, a toxic by-product of metabolism, into oxygen and water.

Students investigated the effect of temperature on the activity of catalase. They measured the oxygen given off at different temperatures by catalase from potato tissue and liver tissue, as shown in the table.

Temp in °C	Rate of oxygen production in cm^3 per minute	
	potato	liver
5	0	4
15	16	8
25	17	21
35	11	46
45	2	44
55	0	37

a) Plot a line graph on a graph grid 11 cm × 11 cm to show the results of their investigation. Use a ruler to join the points with straight lines. *(6)*

b) The temperature at which an enzyme works best is called the optimum temperature. How does the optimum temperature for liver catalase differ from that for potato catalase? *(2)*

c) Both enzymes show a decrease in activity at temperatures higher than the optimum. Explain the reason for this. *(3)*

(Total = 11 marks)

Student 1 response Total 7/11	Examiner comments
a) 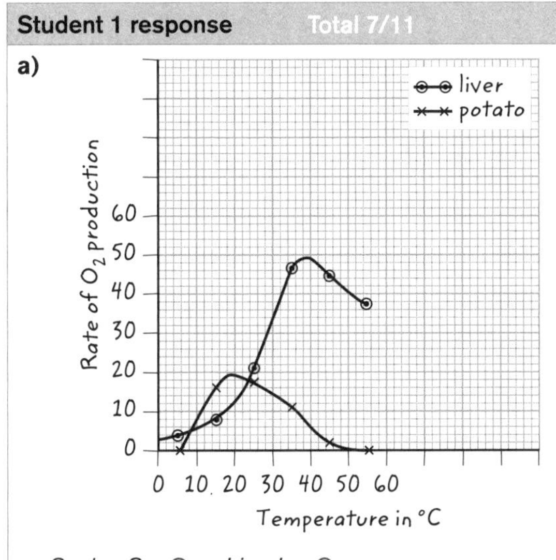 *Scales S = O Line L = O* *Axes (correct way round) A1 = ✔* *Axes (labelled + units) A2 = O* *Points accurate P = ✔ Key K = ✔*	S: scale too small, uses less than half of the grid, so difficult to plot points without making mistakes. L: no mark because line drawn as a curve, but instructed to join points with straight lines. You must be careful to follow the instructions, which may be different for different subjects. For biological data it is nearly always correct to join the points with straight lines. No value provided for temperature 0 °C, so incorrect to start the liver graph at zero. A1: the independent variable (the one you choose to change) is temperature, in this case. The independent variable always goes on the horizontal or *x*-axis. A2: no mark because units not given for vertical axis. P: points plotted accurately. You will find it easier to plot the points if you choose a larger scale and intervals that are easy to count. K: if you are plotting more than one set of data on the axes you must label the lines or give a key.
b) Optimum temperature is 18 °C for potato catalase and 39 °C ✔ for liver. The liver temperature is 21 °C higher ✔ than the one for potato.	The student drew a curve to join the points, instead of using straight lines as instructed. The values quoted are different from those in the mark scheme but have been read correctly from the student's graph, so full credit has been given.

(continued)

c) *Enzymes are protein molecules ✔ and are denatured ✔ at high temperatures.*	The mark allocation (3) shows you that three points have to be made. For full marks the student needs to explain what 'denatured' means in terms of the active site or catalytic action.

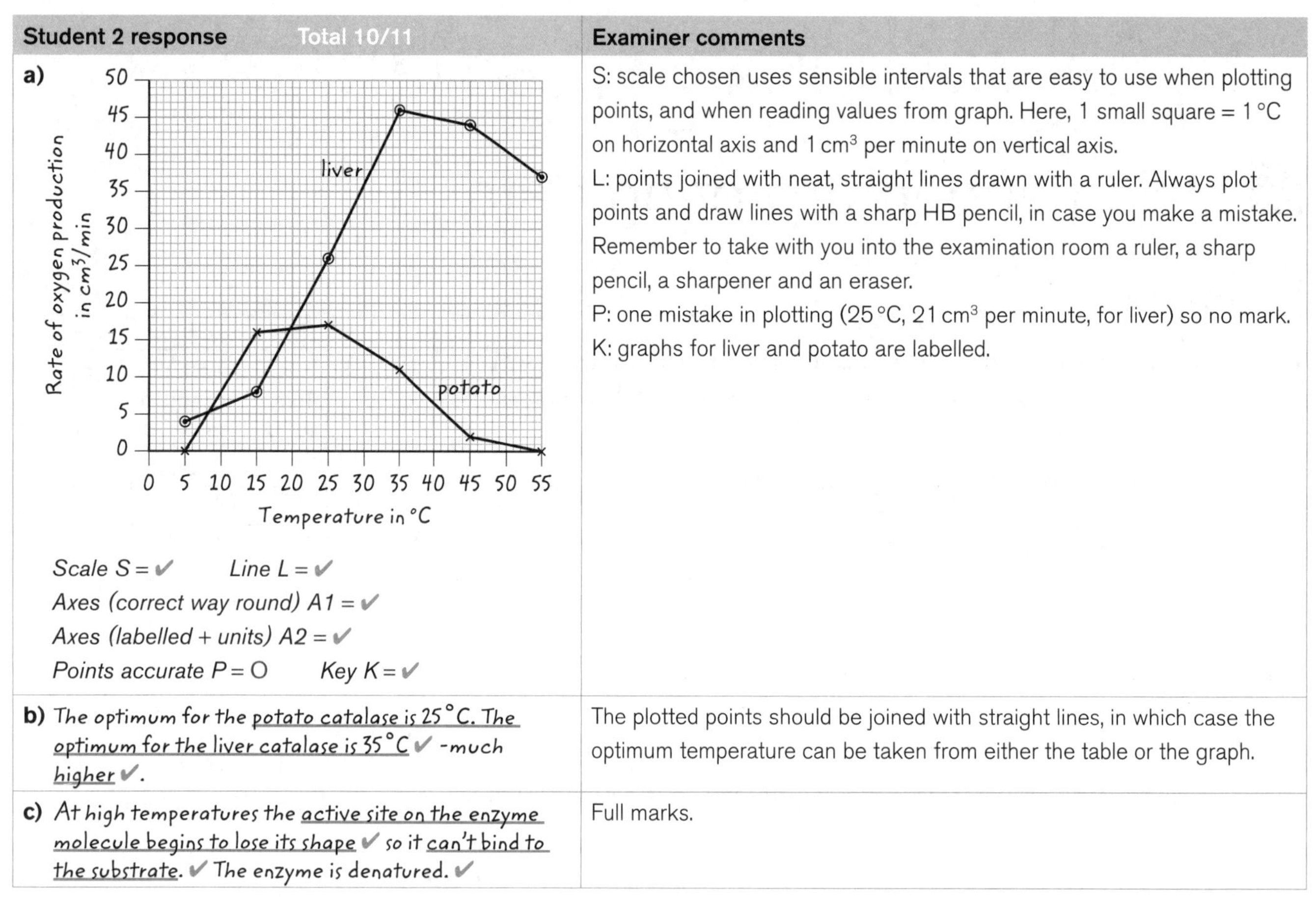

Student 2 response Total 10/11	**Examiner comments**
a) [graph] *Scale S = ✔ Line L = ✔ Axes (correct way round) A1 = ✔ Axes (labelled + units) A2 = ✔ Points accurate P = O Key K = ✔*	S: scale chosen uses sensible intervals that are easy to use when plotting points, and when reading values from graph. Here, 1 small square = 1 °C on horizontal axis and 1 cm³ per minute on vertical axis. L: points joined with neat, straight lines drawn with a ruler. Always plot points and draw lines with a sharp HB pencil, in case you make a mistake. Remember to take with you into the examination room a ruler, a sharp pencil, a sharpener and an eraser. P: one mistake in plotting (25 °C, 21 cm³ per minute, for liver) so no mark. K: graphs for liver and potato are labelled.
b) *The optimum for the potato catalase is 25 °C. The optimum for the liver catalase is 35 °C ✔ - much higher ✔.*	The plotted points should be joined with straight lines, in which case the optimum temperature can be taken from either the table or the graph.
c) *At high temperatures the active site on the enzyme molecule begins to lose its shape ✔ so it can't bind to the substrate. ✔ The enzyme is denatured. ✔*	Full marks.

Practice questions

2 A student was asked to find out whether differences in pH had an effect on the activity of an enzyme that digests protein. The enzyme used was one that is found in the stomach of mammals.

Seven test tubes, each containing a protein solution plus 2% solutions of the enzyme, were placed in a water bath kept at 37 °C. The solutions covered a range of pH from 3 to 9. At the end of the experiment, the student calculated the rate at which a standard amount of protein had been digested in each tube.

The results are shown in the table.

pH	Rate of protein breakdown in arbitrary units
3	100
4	96
5	81
6	60
7	5
8	0
9	0

a) Plot a graph of these results on a graph grid 11 cm × 11 cm. Join the points with straight lines. *(4)*

b) Use the graph to estimate the pH at which the rate of protein breakdown would have been 70 arbitrary units. *(1)*

c) i) At which pH does the enzyme used in the experiment work best? *(1)*

ii) Explain, using the term **active site**, why the activity of the enzyme changes with changes in pH. *(3)*

d) Suggest how the results for pH 4 would be different if the experiment was carried out at 20 °C. Explain your answer. *(3)*

(Total = 12 marks)

3 A student investigated the effect of different concentrations of salt solution on the mass of potato cylinders. He cut potato cylinders from a fresh potato using a cork borer. He blotted each cylinder to remove excess water and weighed it.

He then put each cylinder into a beaker containing salt (sodium chloride) solution for one hour. The student removed the cylinders, blotted them and re-weighed them. For each cylinder he noted the change in mass and converted it to a percentage. His results are shown in the table.

Concentration of salt solution in moles	Initial mass in g	Final mass in g	Change in mass in g	Percentage change in mass
0.0 (water)	2.1	2.6	+0.5	+24
0.1	1.9	2.2	+0.3	**?**
0.2	2.0	2.1	**?**	+5
0.4	2.2	1.8	**?**	−18
0.6	2.0	1.4	−0.6	−30
0.8	1.9	1.1	−0.8	−42

Note: Molarity (moles) is a measure of concentration

a) Some of the data are missing from the table.

i) Calculate the changes in mass of the potato cylinders in 0.2 M and 0.4 M salt solution. *(2)*

ii) Calculate the percentage change in mass for the potato cylinder in 0.1 M salt solution. *(2)*

b) The student drew a line graph of the results.

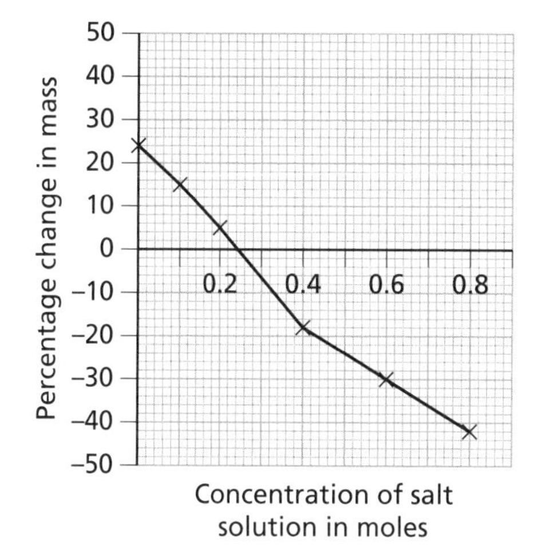

Use information from the graph to answer the following questions.

i) What is the percentage change in mass of the potato cylinder in 0.5 M salt solution? *(1)*

ii) In what concentration of salt solution would potato cylinders neither gain nor lose mass? *(1)*

iii) Over what range of salt concentrations did the potato cylinders lose mass? *(1)*

c) Use your knowledge of osmosis to explain why potato cylinders in these solutions lost mass. *(3)*

(Total = 10 marks)

4 Lipid (fat) molecules form an important part of the human diet. They are digested in the alimentary canal by the enzyme lipase.

a) The reaction is very slow without lipase but very rapid when the enzyme is present. Explain how the enzyme molecule helps speed up the reaction. *(2)*

b) The graph shows the effect of temperature on the rate at which lipase breaks down the fat in milk.

i) At what temperature did the enzyme lipase work best? *(1)*

ii) From the graph, find the rate of the reaction at 20 °C. How does this differ from the rate at 30 °C? *(2)*

iii) Suggest an explanation for the difference. *(2)*

iv) The rate of reaction was very slow at 55 °C. Suggest a reason for this. *(2)*

c) In the small intestine of humans, bile salts produced by the liver are released onto the food. How do the bile salts help to increase the rate at which lipase breaks down lipids? *(2)*

(Total = 11 marks)

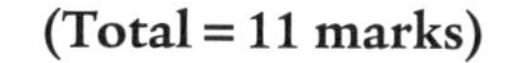

Practical activities

Example

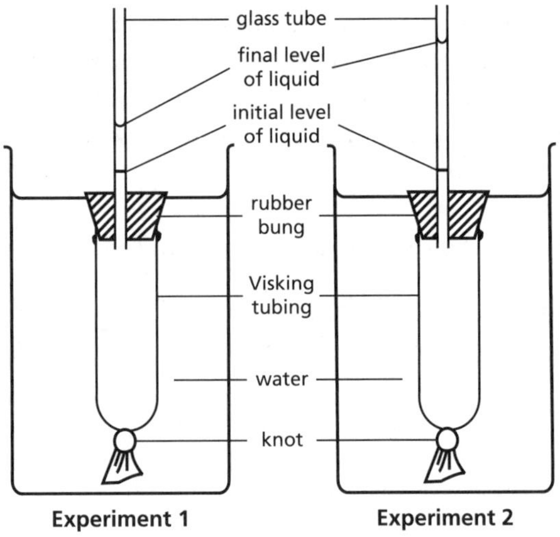

1 John used the apparatus shown in the diagram to demonstrate an important biological process.

He prepared two bags made of Visking tubing (partially permeable dialysis tubing). He then put 50 cm^3 dilute sucrose (sugar) solution into one bag and the same volume of concentrated sucrose solution into the other bag. He tied the bags firmly to the rubber bung and suspended them at the same height in beakers of distilled water. John marked the level of liquid in each glass tube at the start of the experiment and again after 30 minutes. He recorded his results in a table.

a) Suggest how John would measure the level of the liquid to obtain his results. *(2)*

b) i) For Experiment 1, describe the change in the liquid level after 30 minutes. *(1)*

ii) Suggest an explanation for this change in level. *(3)*

c) From the changes in the liquid levels in Experiments 1 and 2, which Visking tubing bag contained the more concentrated sucrose solution? Explain your answer. *(2)*

d) Suggest **one** possible source of error in using this apparatus, and a precaution John might take to overcome it. *(2)*

e) For the comparison to be valid suggest **one** factor that John should keep the same. *(1)*

(Total = 11 marks)

Student 1 response Total 4/11	Marker comments and tips for success
a) *He would measure the height* O *with a ruler,* ✔ *in mm.*	No mark for 'measure the height' because the student didn't explain where to measure the height from – the initial water level. 1 mark for 'with a ruler', but no extra mark for the unit of measurement, mm, because this is an alternative to 'ruler' in the mark scheme.
b) i) *The water level has dropped.* O	The student has not read the labels on the diagram that show the 'final level' is higher than the initial level. The student has called the liquid in the glass tube 'water' (it is a solution of sucrose), a serious mistake in an osmosis question.
ii) *The sucrose has moved out of the Visking tubing bag into the water by osmosis,* O *down the concentration gradient.* O	Sucrose molecules are too large to pass through the small pores in the Visking tubing. No mark for 'osmosis' because the term was used incorrectly. It can only be used to describe the movement of water through partially permeable membranes. No mark for 'concentration gradient' as not describing the movement of water.
c) *Experiment 2. The water level has fallen most.* O	The water level has risen, not fallen. The marks are given for the explanation, so no mark for simply identifying Experiment 2.
d) *He might not have read the bottom of the meniscus.* ✔ *He should keep his eyes level with the meniscus* ✔ *in the glass tubing to read the height on the ruler.*	The answer gives realistic practical details. Other possible answers are given in full in the online mark scheme. They include measuring the bags with a ruler to make sure that they are the same size, and washing the bags after filling to remove any spilt sucrose.
e) *Temperature of the water.* ✔	Correct

Student 2 response Total 10/11	Marker comments and tips for success
a) He would measure the distance from the initial level ✔ in mm. ✔	Correct reference to the liquid level.
b) i) The liquid level in the glass tube has moved up. ✔	Correct
ii) Water molecules have moved into the Visking tubing bag, ✔ which is partially permeable, ✔ by osmosis, ✔ so the volume inside the bag increases. The water molecules move down the concentration gradient.	The student knows the definition of osmosis and has quoted relevant phrases to explain the results. The mark scheme credits other valid points, such as correct reference to movement along a concentration gradient, but only to the maximum mark (3) for the question.
c) Experiment 2. The liquid level has risen further. ✔ There is a bigger difference in concentration between the solution in the bag and the distilled water ✔ outside so the water molecules move into the bag more quickly.	A good answer. Maximum 2 marks awarded.
d) The knot in the tubing might not be tied properly. ✔	This is just enough for 1 mark. The student hasn't explained why this could lead to error (the liquid could leak out) or what precaution to take (tighten the knot firmly from the cut end). You should try to explain your answers precisely to gain full marks.
e) The temperature of the air around the beakers. ✔	Correct

Practice questions

2 A group of students carried out an investigation into the effect of temperature on the activity of the enzyme amylase.

They set up a series of water baths at different temperatures. In each water bath they placed two test tubes. One contained 1 cm^3 of 1% amylase solution and one contained 5 cm^3 of 1% starch solution, as shown in diagram 1.

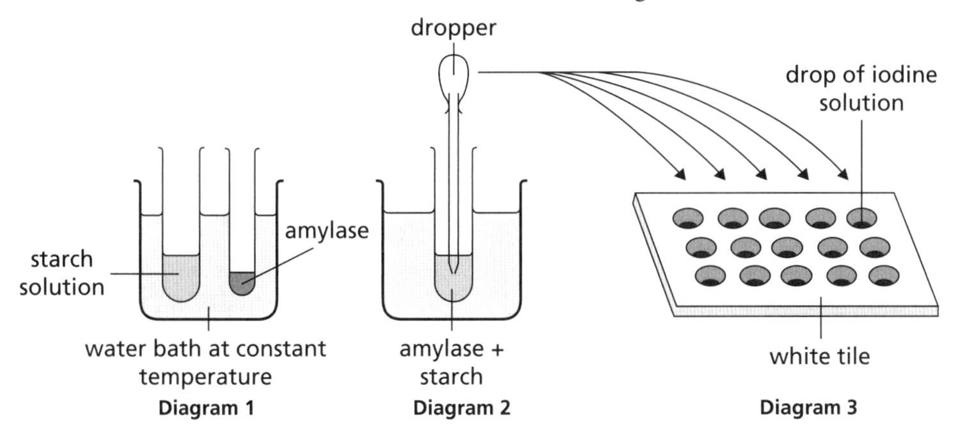

Diagram 1 **Diagram 2** **Diagram 3**

The students then carried out the following steps in their procedure.

1. They left the test tubes in the water baths for at least 10 minutes.
2. They then poured the amylase into the starch solution and mixed the contents (diagram 2).
3. They started the stop clock and added one drop from the tube in each water bath to a drop of iodine solution on a white tile.
4. They tested a drop from each tube in a similar way every 30 seconds, as shown in diagram 3. They used a separate dropper for each tube.
5. They recorded the time until the iodine solution stayed yellow.

a) i) Suggest why they carried out step 1. *(1)*

ii) Give a reason for using a separate dropper for each tube (step 4). *(1)*

b) The students repeated the experiment three times at each temperature and recorded their results in a table.

Temperature of water bath in °C	Time until starch completely digested in minutes			Mean time for starch to be completely digested in minutes
0	Starch present all the time			Starch present all the time
10	12	11	10	11
20	9	6	9	8
30	4	4	5	4.3
40	2	3	3	2.7
50	14	13	15	**?**
60	Starch present all the time			Starch present all the time

i) Identify one anomalous result in the table and suggest a reason for this result. *(2)*

ii) Calculate the mean time for the starch to be completely digested at 50 °C. *(2)*

iii) What was the dependent variable in this investigation? *(1)*

c) i) The temperature at which amylase works best is called the optimum temperature. From the students' results, what was the optimum temperature for amylase? *(1)*

ii) Suggest how the students could obtain a more precise value for the optimum temperature. *(1)*

d) Describe a test for glucose that the students could carry out. *(3)*

(Total = 12 marks)

3 A student cut two cubes, A and B, from a block of colourless jelly. The sides of cube A were 1 cm and the sides of cube B were 3 cm.

The cubes were used as models of living organisms. The student submerged each cube in a red dye for 10 minutes. He then removed it and cut it in half. The diagram shows how far the dye had diffused into the jelly cubes.

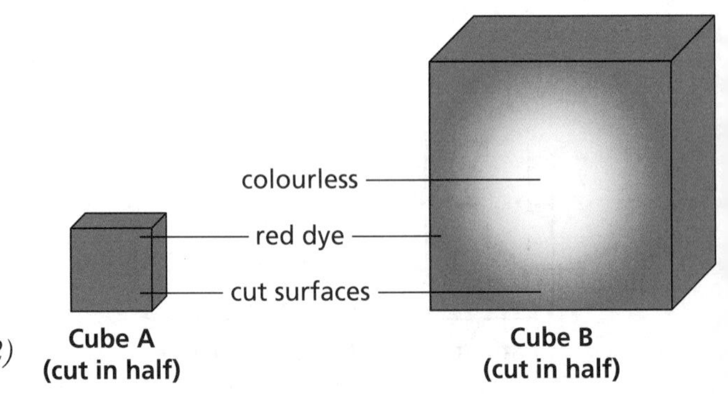

a) Explain what is meant by the term **diffusion**. *(2)*

b) Cube A (sides 1 cm) had a surface area of 6 cm^2 and a volume of 1 cm^3.

i) Calculate the surface area and the volume of cube B (sides 3 cm). *(2)*

ii) Using these values for surface area and volume, explain the results shown in the diagram. *(2)*

c) On the diagram of cube B, shade in and label the area you would expect the dye to reach if the experiment had been carried out at 30 °C rather than 20 °C. Give an explanation for your answer. *(2)*

d) A small organism such as an amoeba can obtain the oxygen it needs by diffusion. Explain why a larger organism, such as an earthworm, needs a transport system so that oxygen can reach all the cells in the body. *(2)*

(Total = 10 marks)

Understanding structure, function and processes

Example

1 a) The diagram shows a fungus (*Mucor*) that often grows on stale bread.

i) Describe **three** structural features of *Mucor* that are typical of a fungus. *(3)*

ii) Describe how a fungus such as *Mucor* obtains nutrients from the bread. *(2)*

iii) List **three** characteristics, other than feeding and growing, that *Mucor* shares with other living organisms. *(3)*

(magnification ×20)

b) The structure of *Mucor* can be seen with a light microscope, but for some microorganisms, such as bacteria and viruses, an electron microscope is needed to see the detail. Give **three** ways in which bacteria differ in structure from viruses. *(3)*

(Total = 11 marks)

Student 1 response Total 7/11	**Marker comments and tips for success**
a) i) *It is made up of colourless threads called hyphae.* ✔ *It has no chlorophyll and is not green.* O *The hyphae aren't divided into cells so there are lots of nuclei.* ✔	The question asks for structural features, so the colour and lack of chlorophyll are not credited.
ii) *Fungi feed by saprotrophic nutrition.* ✔ *The hyphae grow on the bread and digest it.* O	Just misses a second mark. Response needs a reference to enzymes or a clearer description of digestion 'outside the hyphae'.
iii) *It breathes* O *and excretes* ✔ *and reproduces.* ✔	All living things respire, which means that they obtain energy from the breakdown of glucose. Learn the correct terms to use in biology, 'respiration', 'ventilation' and 'gas exchange', so you can avoid using the word 'breathing' in your answers.
b) *Bacteria are cells* ✔ *and have a cell membrane.* ✔ *Viruses are parasites but bacteria can live on their own.* O	Two marks for bacteria having a cellular structure and cell membrane. Viruses are all parasitic, but this is not a structural difference, so no mark.

Student 2 response Total 10/11	**Marker comments and tips for success**
a) i) *Mucor has a mycelium* ✔ *of threads, which have walls made of chitin.* ✔ *The nuclei are dotted in the cytoplasm.* ✔	'Nuclei dotted in the cytoplasm' is equivalent to 'many nuclei'.
ii) *The Mucor secretes enzymes that digest the bread.* ✔ *The small molecules from digestion are absorbed* ✔ *by the hyphae.*	This is a clear and concise answer, helped by the use of the correct terms, such as 'secrete'. This section about 'Variety of living organisms' is very short so you should be able to remember the correct terms to use.
iii) *Respiration,* ✔ *excreting metabolic wastes* ✔ *and movement.* ✔	Like other living organisms, fungi do move, usually by growth.
b) *Bacteria have a nucleus but viruses don't.* O *Bacteria have plasmids but viruses don't.* ✔ *Bacteria have a circular chromosome* ✔ *but viruses just have DNA.*	Bacteria do not have a nucleus, so no mark for the first point. Although the student has said enough to gain a mark for the third point, note that she is wrong to state that viruses just have DNA – many contain RNA instead.

Practice questions

2 a) The diagram shows three human cheek cells. Name the parts labelled A, B and C. *(3)*

b) Organisms are made up of cells, and are organised into organs, systems and tissues. In the table, list these four levels of organisation in order of increasing complexity. Write down **one** example of each, next to its name. The first one has been done for you. *(3)*

Level of organisation	Example
1 cell	cheek cell
2	
3	
4	

c) Give **two** ways in which the structure of a yeast cell (a fungus) is similar to the structure of an animal cell, such as a cheek cell, and **one** way in which it differs. *(3)*

(Total = 9 marks)

3 a) The diagram shows a cell from a leaf.

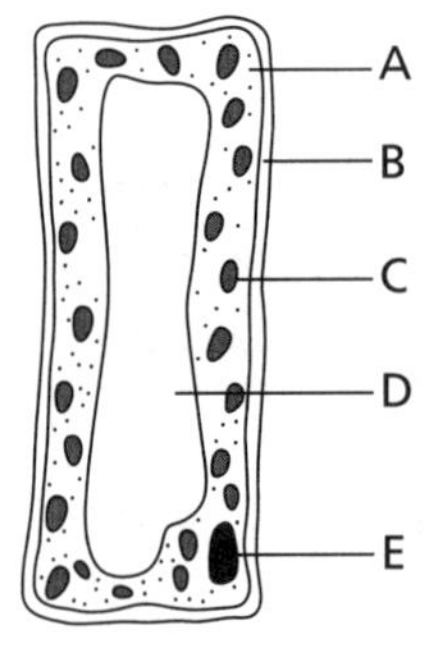

In the table below, name parts **A**, **B**, **C**, **D** and **E**. For each part, describe **one** main function. *(5)*

Part	Name	Function
A		
B		
C		
D		
E		

b) Describe **two** ways in which the structure of the leaf cell is similar to the structure of an animal cell, such as a cheek cell, and **two** ways in which it is different. *(4)*

(Total = 9 marks)

4 a) Biologists who study the structure of organisms have placed living things into groups according to their features. Complete the table to show the groups of organisms that have each feature. If the group has a feature put a tick (✔) in the box. If the group does not have a feature put a cross (✗). *(4)*

Feature	Viruses	Bacteria	Protoctists
1 Each organism is a single cell			
2 The organisms can only reproduce inside living cells			
3 The organisms have cell membranes			
4 The organisms contain plasmids			

b) What is the meaning of the term **pathogen**? Name a pathogenic organism from each group (viruses, bacteria an d protoctists). *(4)*

(Total = 8 marks)

Applying principles

Example

1 A student carried out an investigation into the processes that take place inside bean seeds at the start of germination. The beans were divided into three groups:

Group X Beans soaked in water for 48 hours

Group Y Beans soaked for 48 hours then boiled for 15 minutes and cooled

Group Z Beans left in their original dry state

Three Petri dishes containing agar (a jelly) and starch were prepared. They were marked X, Y and Z. Beans from each group were cut in half and placed, cut side down, onto the agar jelly. The plates were kept in an incubator at 25 °C.

After 24 hours, the student removed the beans but used pins to show where the beans had been on the surface of the agar jelly. He poured iodine solution over the agar jelly, gently rinsing it off after 2 minutes. The results are shown in the diagram.

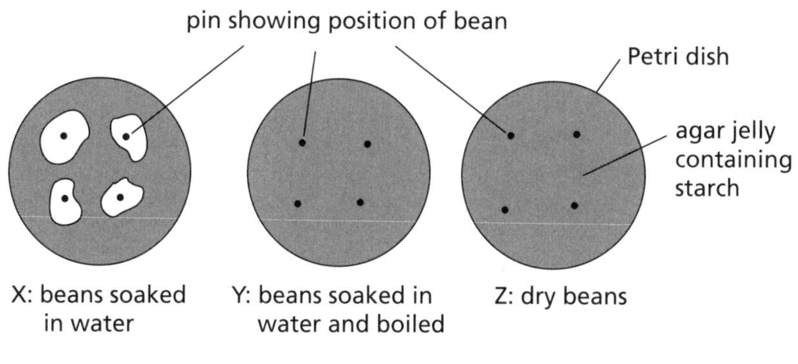

Key ▬ blue-black colour ▭ red-brown colour

a) i) Describe the distribution of starch in dishes X, Y and Z. *(2)*

ii) Suggest an explanation for the distribution of starch in dishes X and Y. *(3)*

iii) Suggest an explanation for the distribution of starch in dish Z. *(2)*

b) The student noticed that the beans soaked in water for 48 hours had begun to germinate, but the dry beans had not.

Give **one** factor, other than water, which is necessary for beans to germinate. *(1)*

(Total = 8 marks)

Student 1 response Total 5/8	Marker comments and tips for success
a) i) *In X there is no starch under the places where the beans were put.* O *In Y starch is in all parts of the dish, and the same for Z.* ✔	Only 1 mark. The student described the areas underneath the beans in dish X but did not say that there was starch in the other parts of the dish.
ii) *The beans in X might have produced something that broke down the starch,* ✔ *but in Y they didn't.* ✔	Even though the student didn't connect the breakdown of starch to production of an enzyme, she was able to gain 2 marks by applying her understanding of starch breakdown to this unfamiliar investigation.
iii) *There is nothing in the dry beans that can break down starch.* ✔	For the second mark the student needed to refer to enzyme action.
b) *A warm temperature.* ✔	Correct

Student 2 response Total 7/8	Marker comments and tips for success
a) i) In X most of the dish contains starch, apart from the areas that were underneath the beans. ✔ These have no starch. In Y and Z there is starch in the whole of the dish. ✔	The answer is clear and concise.
ii) In X the beans produced something like amylase ✔ which broke down the starch. ✔ When they were cooked this didn't work anymore. ✔	In this type of question you are not expected to have studied the investigation yourself. The marks are awarded for the way you apply your knowledge of biology to a new situation. So recognising that the breakdown of starch might be due to something 'like' amylase is enough for a mark.
iii) Unlike X, the dry beans didn't produce any amylase ✔ to break down the starch. ✔	Full marks
b) Light is necessary for germination. O	Light is necessary for plant growth but not for germination.

Practice questions

2 a) The diagram shows the structure of a cell from a potato.

Name the parts of the cell labelled A, B and C. The cell membrane has been labelled for you. *(3)*

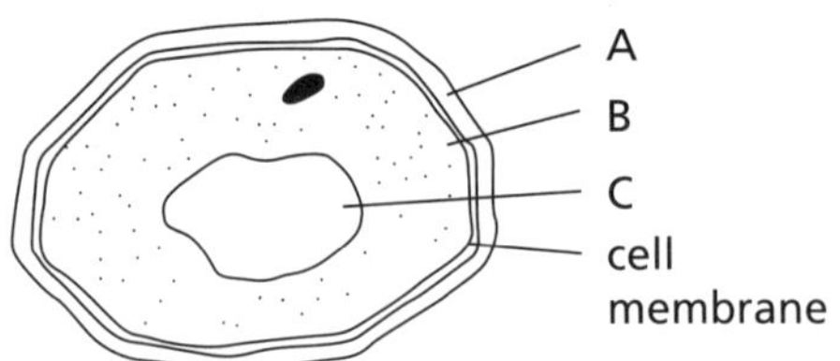

b) A student investigated osmosis in potatoes. She cut a large potato into halves and removed about 1 cm of peel from the edge of the cut surface. She boiled one potato half for 10 minutes then cooled it. She cut a well in the top of each potato half and placed them in dishes of water as shown in diagram 1. The student put 5 cm^3 of concentrated sucrose (sugar) solution inside each well, and left the dishes for 4 hours.

i) Diagram 2 shows the results for the potato halves after 4 hours. Describe the results for the unboiled potato. *(2)*

ii) Suggest an explanation for the results in the unboiled potato. *(3)*

iii) Suggest a reason for the liquid level staying the same in the boiled potato. *(2)*

Diagram 1

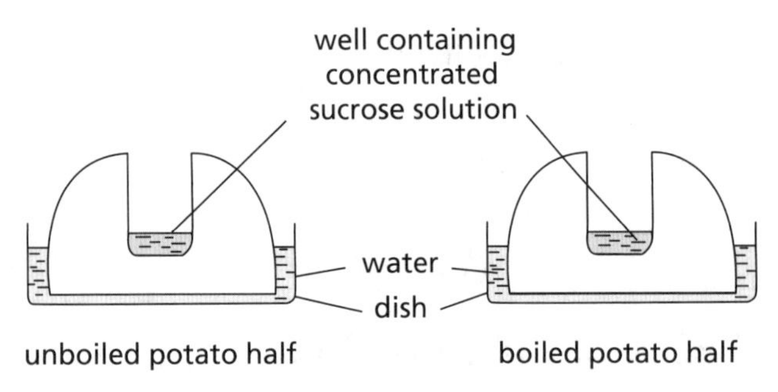

Diagram 2

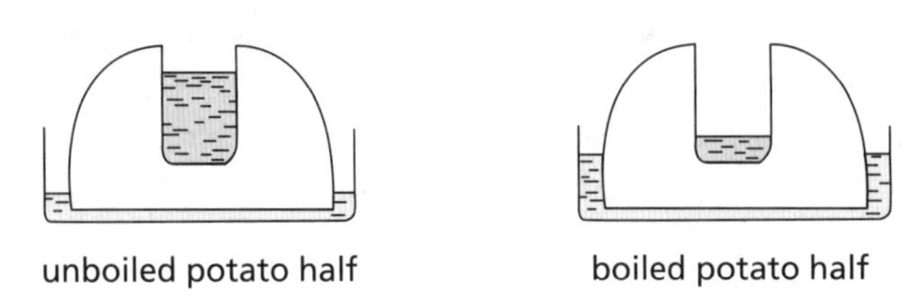

(Total = 10 marks)

3 In an investigation, the effect of osmosis on red blood cells was observed. A drop of blood was placed on each of two microscope slides. On slide A, the blood was mixed with a 0.85% solution of salt (sodium chloride). On slide B, the blood was mixed with a 3.0% solution of salt. Both slides were observed under the microscope.

The appearance of one cell from each slide, at the start and again after a few minutes, is shown in the diagram.

slides A and B
red blood cells at the start of the investigation

slide A
red blood cells after a few minutes in 0.85% salt solution

slide B
red blood cells after a few minutes in 3.0% salt solution

a) i) Describe the appearance of the red blood cells on slides A and B after a few minutes in the salt solutions. *(2)*

ii) Suggest an explanation for the changes in the cells on slide B. *(3)*

iii) The red blood cells circulating in the plasma do not change shape in this way. Suggest a reason for this. *(2)*

b) Red blood cells take up some substances that they need by active transport. How does this differ from osmosis? *(2)*

(Total = 9 marks)

4 A student prepared a starch agar jelly by stirring a solution of starch into hot, liquid agar. It formed a colourless jelly when cooled. She cut the agar jelly into small cubes with sides of 1 cm and large cubes with sides of 2 cm.

She put three cubes of each size into a beaker containing amylase solution. After 30 minutes she removed the cubes and cut each one carefully in half.

She covered the cut surfaces with iodine solution and observed the colour changes. The diagram shows the colour of the cut surface after iodine was added.

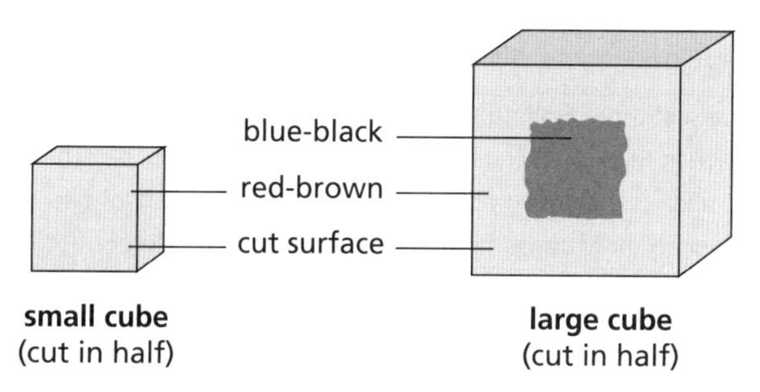

cubes of starch agar jelly after 30 minutes in amylase solution

a) What does the appearance of the small and large cubes suggest about the distribution of starch? *(2)*

b) Suggest an explanation for the results in the small cube. *(2)*

c) Suggest an explanation for the difference in starch distribution between the small and large cubes. *(3)*

(Total = 7 marks)

2 Nutrition and respiration

Using and interpreting data

Example

1 The graph shows how the rate of photosynthesis is affected by altering the concentration of carbon dioxide. The plant is kept at the same light intensity and its rate of photosynthesis is measured at two different temperatures.

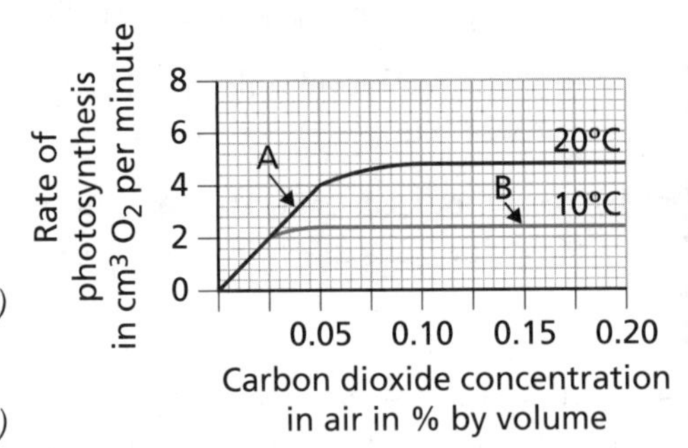

a) Compare the rates of photosynthesis at 20 °C and 10 °C when the carbon dioxide concentration is above 0.15%. *(2)*

b) Give the factor that is limiting the rate of photosynthesis at point **A**. Explain your answer. *(2)*

c) Give the factor that is limiting the rate of photosynthesis at point **B**. Explain your answer. *(2)*

(Total = 6 marks)

Student 1 response Total 3/6	Marker comments and tips for success
a) *The rate at 20 °C is higher than at 10 °C ✔ by 2.1 cm³ O_2 per min.* O	You should quote values from the graph to support your answer, but it is easy to misread the scale. Here, the student stated correctly that one rate was higher than the other. However, the difference is 2.4 cm³ O_2 per minute, not 2.1.
b) *Light is needed for photosynthesis.* O	There are just three limiting factors (carbon dioxide, light intensity and temperature) so try each in turn. In this case, the graph shows that when carbon dioxide concentration is increased above point A, 0.04%, the rate of photosynthesis increases, so low availability of carbon dioxide was limiting the rate of photosynthesis at point A.
c) *Temperature.* ✔	This student correctly identified temperature as the limiting factor but left out the explanation. If you underline all the parts that need answers when you first read through a question you are less likely to miss something out. Underlining also helps you focus on what is required in the answer.

Student 2 response Total 6/6	Marker comments and tips for success
a) *The rate of photosynthesis at 20 °C (4.8 cm³ O_2 per min) is double ✔ that at 10 °C.* ✔	The student gained a mark for quoting values to support the difference between the two rates. By stating the relationship between the two values (one was double the other) the student gained a further mark.
b) *Carbon dioxide is limiting the rate of photosynthesis.* ✔ *When carbon dioxide is increased the rate increases.* ✔	The student shows understanding of limiting factors and their effects. If increasing a factor increases the rate of photosynthesis, that factor (in this case carbon dioxide) was limiting the rate. Practice on graphs like this will improve your own understanding.
c) *Temperature.* ✔ *When the temperature is increased to 20 °C, the carbon dioxide concentration staying the same, the rate of photosynthesis is higher.* ✔	If you look at the graph at B you can eliminate CO_2 as the limiting factor. Altering it has no effect on the rate of photosynthesis at B. However, the graph for the experiment at a higher temperature does show an increased rate, indicating that temperature is limiting the rate at B.

Practice questions

2 Lipids (fats) in the diet are an important source of energy and some provide essential molecules for cell membranes. Butter, margarine and low-fat spreads are all important sources of fat in people's diets. The graph shows changes in the fats eaten in Britain from 1976 to 1996.

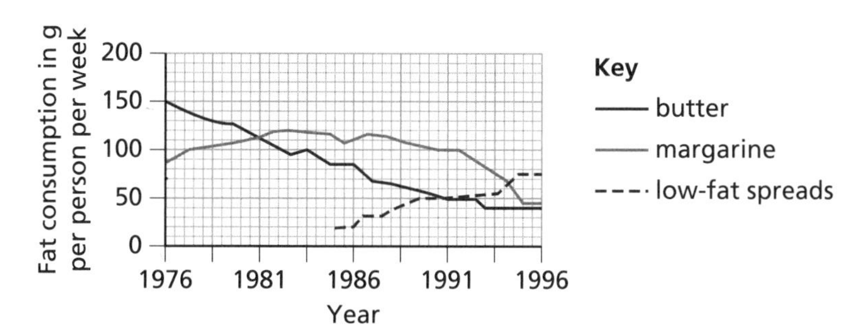

a) i) What was the largest source of fat in the weekly diet in 1976? *(1)*

ii) The total fat eaten per person per week in 1976 was 240 g. How many grams came from margarine? *(1)*

iii) From the graph, describe the change in the amount of butter eaten per week over the 20 years from 1976 to 1996. *(2)*

b) i) From the graph, calculate the total fat eaten per person per week in 1991. Give **one** way in which this differed from the total amount of fat eaten per person per week in 1976. *(3)*

ii) Suggest **two** reasons why the amount of fat in the weekly diet in 1996 is better for health than that in 1976. *(2)*

(Total = 9 marks)

3 Students in a class used the apparatus shown to measure the energy content of different foods.

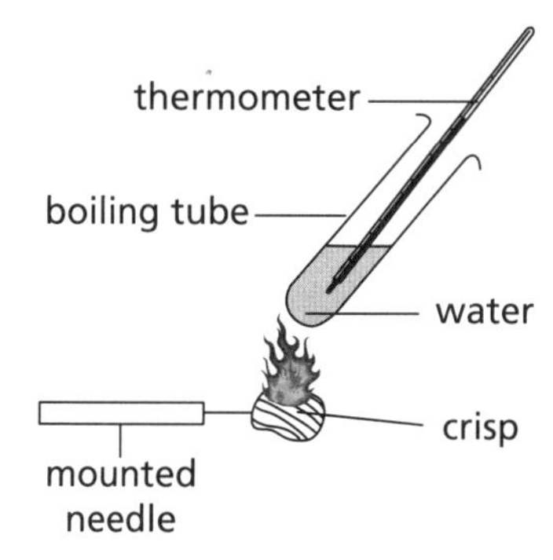

One student investigated the energy value of potato crisps. She put 20 cm^3 of water into the boiling tube. She then weighed one of the crisps, set it alight with a Bunsen burner and quickly held it underneath the boiling tube. She recorded the original temperature of the water, and the temperature immediately after the crisp finished burning.
The student used the formula below to calculate the energy released when one crisp was burned.

Energy in joules = mass of water × rise in temperature × 4.2

Note: 4.2 joules = the energy required to raise the temperature of 1 g of water by 1 °C. 1 cm^3 of water has a mass of 1 g.

a) i) The initial temperature of the water was 20 °C, and the final temperature 52 °C. Calculate the energy, in joules, released when the crisp was burned. *(3)*

ii) The mass of the crisp was 0.8 g. Calculate the energy released per g of crisps. *(1)*

b) i) The results obtained by the students for other foods are shown in the table.

Food	Energy per g in joules
rice cakes	1600
crispbread	1450
raisins	1300

Calculate the difference in energy released when 1 g of rice cake is burnt compared with 1 g of raisins. *(2)*

ii) The students saw that the energy value of the rice cakes was given on the packaging as 1582 kJ per 100 g. Suggest a reason for the difference between the results obtained by the students and the actual value. *(2)*

(Total = 8 marks)

4 The carbohydrate, lipid and protein content in 10 g of two foods is shown in the table.

Food	Mass in g per 10 g portion		
	carbohydrate	lipid	protein
White bread	4.8	0.2	0.7
Eggs (boiled)	0.0	1.1	1.3

a) A slice of bread weighs 40 g. An athlete in training is advised to include about 116 g of carbohydrate per meal. How many slices of bread would provide this? *(3)*

b) The athlete was advised to include about 77 g protein in his diet every day.

i) Explain why an athlete needs protein. *(2)*

ii) What is the percentage of protein in white bread? *(2)*

iii) Suggest why it would be preferable for the athlete to obtain the protein he needs from foods other than bread. Give reasons to support your answer. *(2)*

(Total = 9 marks)

Practical activities

Example

1 Sam investigated the energy content of different snacks. To determine the energy content of potato crisps, he used the apparatus shown.

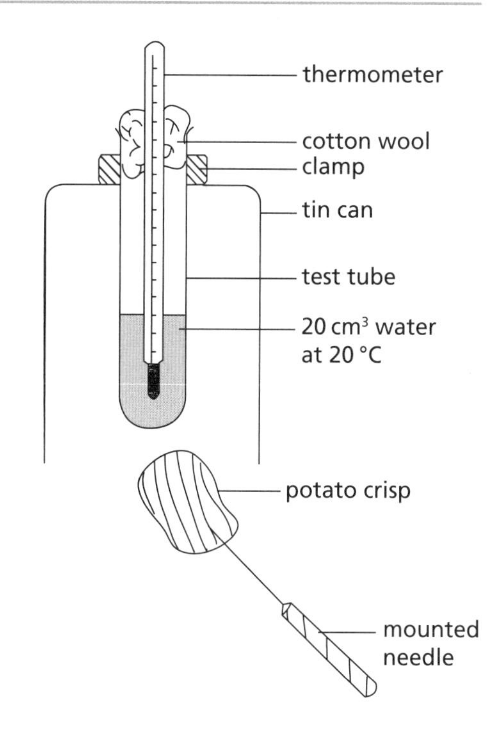

He weighed one of the crisps. He set light to it with a Bunsen burner and quickly held it underneath the test tube. He recorded the rise in temperature of the water in the test tube and used this to calculate the energy released when one crisp was burnt.

a) Sam used some special features in his apparatus to help him obtain more accurate results. These are listed below. For each feature, suggest how it would help him obtain more accurate results:

i) He used a test tube with thinner glass walls than usual. *(1)*

ii) He surrounded the test tube of water with a tin can. *(1)*

iii) He placed cotton wool in the opening of the test tube. *(1)*

b) Suggest **two** other sources of error that Sam did not take into account. *(2)*

c) Suggest **one** way that Sam could improve the reliability of his results. *(1)*

(Total = 6 marks)

Student 1 response Total 3/6	Marker comments and tips for success
a) i) *The water in the test tube would get hotter ✓ because the heat has less glass to travel through.*	The student has understood that more energy has transferred to the water (it gets hotter) than if a test tube of thicker glass was used.
ii) *The can traps the hot smoke ✓ so the water gets hotter.*	The student has conveyed the idea of heat being trapped and has also explained how this links to a higher water temperature (indicating increased accuracy).
iii) *The cotton wool stops contaminants falling in the water and affecting the results.* O	Cotton wool can have different uses in biology experiments. Here it prevents warm air rising and leaving the tube. In other situations it is used to prevent microorganisms from the air entering the apparatus, or it can be used as an insulator.
b) *There might not have been enough oxygen in the air for the crisp to burn properly.* O *The glass thermometer would itself absorb heat.* ✓	One mark. If the crisp was held higher in the can then this first statement might be true. However, the diagram clearly shows the crisp being held below the can. You must look carefully at the information given.
c) *He could have used an electronic thermometer to get more accurate temperature readings.* O	The student has confused accuracy with reliability. Accuracy depends on the quality of the measuring apparatus. Reliability can only be improved if the experiment is repeated several times and the variation in the results recorded.

Student 2 response Total 5/6	Marker comments and tips for success
a) i) *There would be less glass to heat up ✔ so the water would get hotter.*	The student has understood that the experiment will be more accurate if heat loss can be reduced, and that if less glass has to be heated up more heat energy will be transferred to the water and the recorded temperature will be higher.
ii) *Less heat lost to the air ✔ so more heating of the water and the temperature rises.*	The student has understood that the can reduces heat loss to the surrounding air.
iii) *The cotton wool traps the heat. ✔*	The student has said just enough for the mark.
b) *Part of the crisp might not have burnt, ✔ or left soot O, so the value for the heat produced would be too low.*	Only 1 mark here because soot is left when something doesn't burn completely, i.e. it is the same marking point.
c) *He could repeat the experiment several times and calculate the mean result. ✔*	For the results to be reliable they should be repeatable and show little variation. Experiments should be repeated a minimum of three times to check that there is very little variation between the outcomes. The mean result can then be calculated.

Practice questions

2 A student investigated the factors needed for a plant to carry out photosynthesis. He used a plant that had been kept in the dark for two days. He covered some of the leaves with bags, as follows:

Leaf 1: Transparent polythene bag containing air

Leaf 2: Transparent polythene bag containing air and a substance that absorbs carbon dioxide

Leaf 3: Black polythene bag containing air

a) Why does a plant become 'destarched' when left in the dark for two days? *(1)*

b) Name a substance that could be used to absorb carbon dioxide. *(1)*

c) The student left the plant in the light for eight hours, then took the leaves off the plant and tested them for starch. The steps he used are shown in the diagram.

Step 1
Leaf dipped in boiling water
↓
Step 2
Leaf boiled in ethanol
↓
Step 3
Leaf dipped in hot water
↓
Step 4
Leaf spread on a white tile and covered with iodine solution

i) In step 1, why is the leaf dipped in boiling water? *(1)*

ii) 1 What is the purpose of step 2? *(1)*

2 Describe **two** precautions that should be taken when carrying out step 2. *(2)*

iii) In step 4, what colour would the leaf be if starch was present, and if starch was absent? *(2)*

d) The table shows the results of the starch tests.

	Leaf 1	Leaf 2	Leaf 3
Starch present	✓	×	×

Write a suitable conclusion for these results. *(2)*

(Total = 10 marks)

3 A student investigated the rate of photosynthesis at different temperatures. For Experiment 1, she set up the apparatus shown in the diagram and counted the number of bubbles of oxygen produced per minute at each temperature. A lamp placed near the apparatus provided light.

For Experiment 2 the student moved the lamp 10 cm closer to the beaker and repeated the readings.

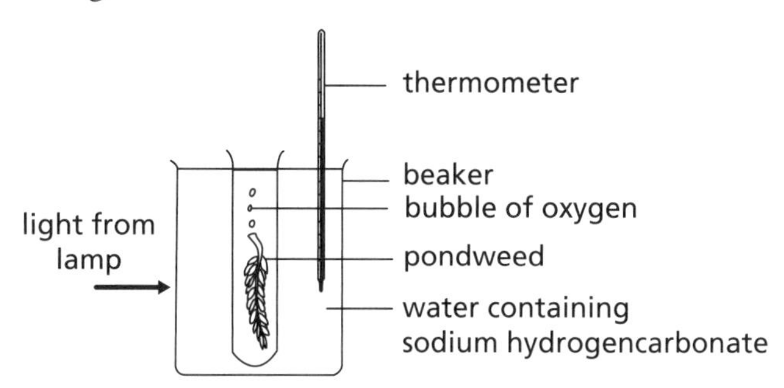

a) Why did the student add sodium hydrogencarbonate to the water in the test tube? *(1)*

The student took five readings at each temperature and recorded the mean number of bubbles per minute in a table.

Temperature in °C	Number of bubbles per min	
	Exp 1	**Exp 2**
5	15.0	15.2
10	21.2	21.8
15	27.0	27.6
20	29.0	34.0
25	28.6	38.2
30	29.0	42.0

b) i) Plot a graph of the data (on a graph grid 9 cm × 9 cm) using straight lines to join the points. *(6)*

ii) From your graph, what is the rate of photosynthesis at 18 °C (in bubbles per minute) for Experiment 1 and Experiment 2? *(2)*

c) i) Describe the differences between the two graphs for temperatures between 20 °C and 30 °C. *(2)*

ii) Suggest an explanation for the differences. *(2)*

d) Suggest **one** precaution that the student could take to ensure that the results are as accurate as possible. *(1)*

(Total = 14 marks)

4 The apparatus below can be used to show that germinating peas give off carbon dioxide.

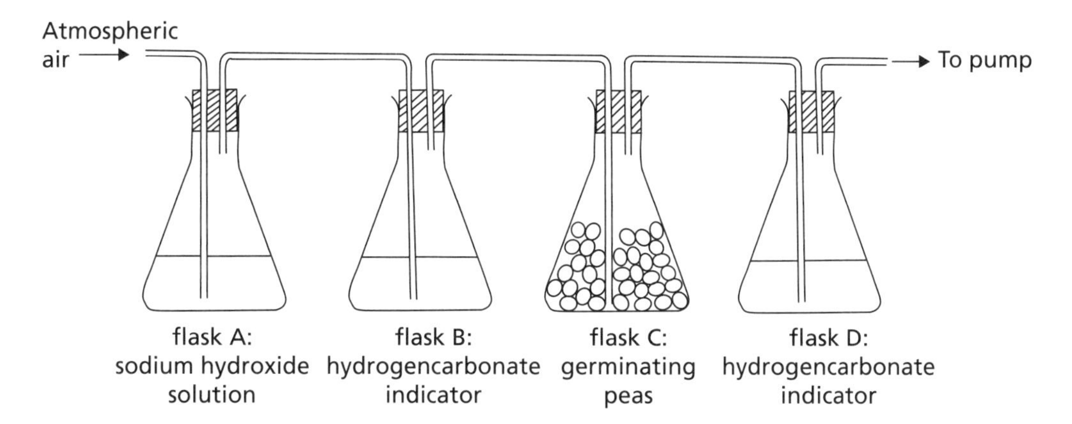

The flasks are set up with the contents shown. The sodium hydroxide solution absorbs carbon dioxide from the air.

a) i) At the start, before the pump was turned on, the hydrogencarbonate indicator solutions in flasks B and D were orange in colour. What does this suggest about the concentration of carbon dioxide in the flasks? *(1)*

ii) Describe, with reasons, the colour you would expect to see in flasks B and D after the apparatus had been running for 45 minutes. *(4)*

b) Describe how you would alter this apparatus to show that germinating peas release heat. *(2)*

(Total = 7 marks)

5 Sara set up the apparatus shown to measure the rate of respiration of living organisms at different temperatures. She did two experiments, the first with maggots and the second with peas. The respiration rate can be measured by recording the rate at which the coloured water rises in the glass tube.

Experiment 1: Sara put eight maggots into the boiling tube.

She made sure that the level of the coloured water in the glass tube was level with the water outside the tube, at the start. After 30 minutes she measured the height that the water had risen to. She repeated this at different temperatures and recorded the results.

Experiment 2: Sara repeated the experiment, replacing the maggots with an equivalent mass of peas that had been soaked in water overnight.

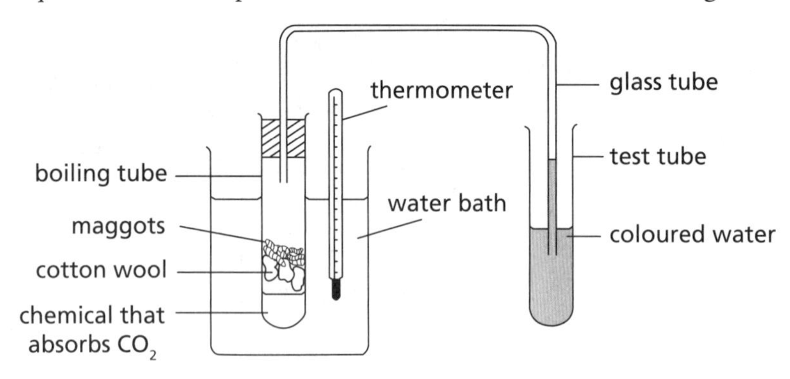

a) i) Name a chemical that absorbs carbon dioxide. *(1)*

ii) Explain why the level of coloured water in the glass tube rises. *(2)*

b) Sara's results for both experiments are shown in the table.

The results for the maggots have been plotted in the graph below. On the same graph, plot the results Sara obtained for the peas, joining the points with straight lines. *(2)*

Temperature in °C	Height of water in mm	
	Exp 1 Maggots	Exp 2 Peas
5	8	3
10	12	5
15	17	7
20	23	11
25	31	17

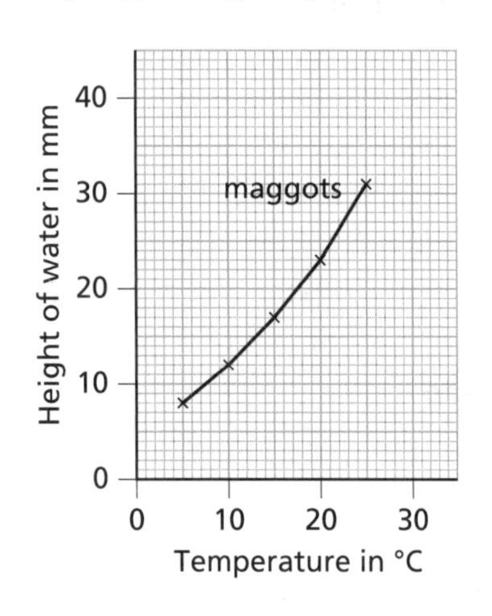

c) i) What was the rate of respiration of the maggots (in mm/min) at 20 °C? *(2)*

ii) From the graph of the results for maggots, suggest what you would expect the water height to be at 30 °C. *(1)*

d) i) How much faster did the maggots respire at 18 °C compared with 8 °C? *(3)*

ii) Give an explanation for this based on your knowledge of enzyme action. *(2)*

(Total = 13 marks)

Understanding structure, function and processes

Example

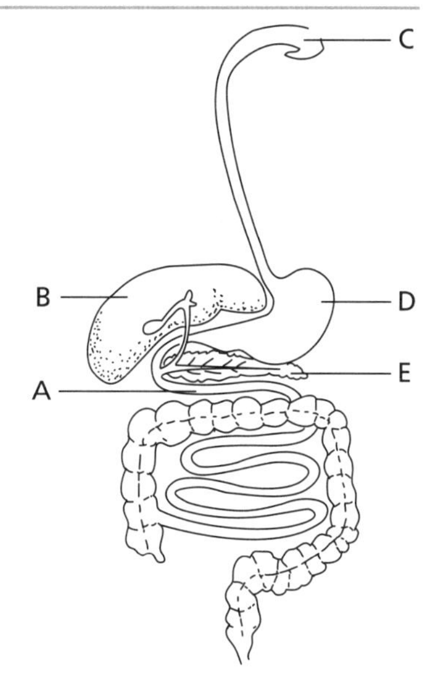

1 The diagram shows part of the human digestive system.

a) The table lists some processes that occur in the digestive system. Complete the table using letters from the diagram to show where each process occurs. Letters may be used more than once. Write **one** letter only in each box. *(4)*

Process	Letter
1 starch is first digested	
2 fat is emulsified	
3 bile is produced	
4 protein is first digested	

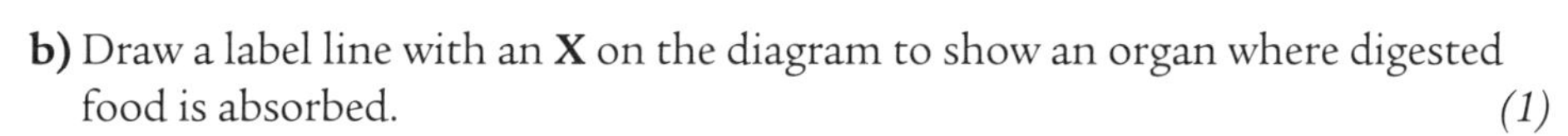

b) Draw a label line with an **X** on the diagram to show an organ where digested food is absorbed. *(1)*

c) i) Name the tube that carries swallowed food to the stomach. *(1)*

ii) Describe how the food is moved along this tube. *(2)*

d) i) Name **two** products of digestion that move from the small intestine into the villi. *(2)*

ii) Explain how the structure of a villus helps absorption of the products of digestion. *(2)*

(Total = 12 marks)

Student 1 response Total 5/12	Marker comments and tips for success
a) 1 C ✔ 2 B A O 3 B ✔ 4 D ✔	No mark for row 2. The student put two letters in this box so the wrong answer (B) negates the right one (A).
b) X O	Label line ends ambiguously, touching two organs, the small intestine and the large intestine, rather than just the small intestine. You must make label lines clear.
c) i) *Trachea* O	The trachea carries air to the lungs. Oesophagus is the correct answer.
ii) *By muscles* O *in the tube.*	For this mark, the student needed to say that muscle contraction moved the food.
d) i) *Fatty acids* ✔ *and sugar molecules* O	The general term 'sugar' should be used with caution. Some 'sugars', such as glucose, do move into the villi, but others, such as sucrose or maltose, do not. Their molecules are larger and need to be digested further.
ii) *The villi are a shape like a finger so molecules are absorbed quickly.* O *Their surface is very thin so molecules don't have far to travel.* ✔	No mark for the first statement because the student did not explain that the shape of the villi increases the surface area.

Student 2 response Total 8/12	Marker comments and tips for success
a) 1 A O 2 A ✔ 3 E O 4 stomach O	1 Starch is first digested in the mouth, C. 3 The student put organ E (the pancreas) instead of the liver, B. You need to be able to recognise the digestive organs from a diagram. 4 The student hasn't identified the stomach as organ D, so no mark.
b) X ✔	The student has angled the label line so it ends accurately on part of the small intestine. Use simple lines like this to label diagrams, rather than arrows.
c) i) oesophagus ✔	Correct
ii) The food is moved along by muscle contraction ✔ in the walls of the tube. This is called peristalsis. ✔	A good answer, gaining full marks.
d) i) Glucose ✔ and amino acids ✔	Full marks.
ii) The villi project from the inside of the small intestine. Their surface area is very large so molecules are absorbed quickly. ✔ They have a good blood supply so that absorbed food can be carried away. O	The question asks how the structure of the villus helps absorption, so the network of capillaries that provides the 'good blood supply' has to be mentioned for the second mark.

Practice questions

2 A teacher set up an experiment to represent the action of the gut. She used a length of partially permeable dialysis tubing (Visking tubing) to represent the gut. The tubing has small pores that allow only small molecules to pass through. She filled the tubing with starch solution mixed with the enzyme amylase, then placed it in water in a beaker. She left the open end hanging over the side of the beaker so that the contents of the tube could be sampled.

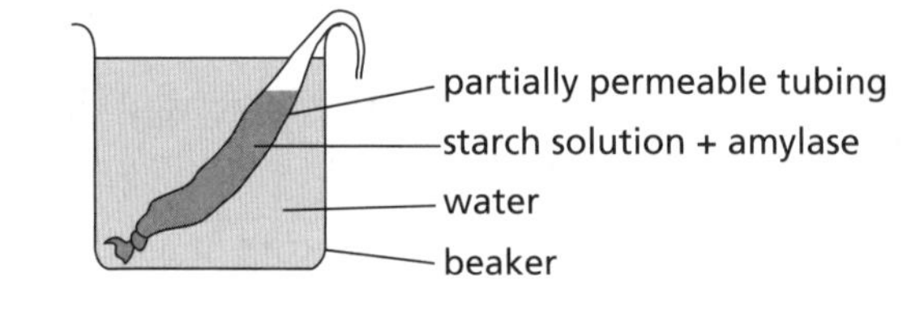

The teacher tested the contents of the tubing and the water in the beaker for starch and for maltose. She did this at the start of the experiment and again after 2 hours. The results are shown in the table. A tick (✓) means that starch or maltose was present and a cross (✗) that they were absent.

Test	At start		After 2 hours	
	inside tubing	**water in beaker**	**inside tubing**	**water in beaker**
Starch	✓	✗	✗	✗
Maltose	✗	✗	✓	✓

a) i) Suggest why starch molecules are found only inside the tubing and not in the water in the beaker. *(1)*

ii) Explain why, after 2 hours, maltose is present inside the tubing. *(2)*

iii) Explain why maltose is present in the water in the beaker after 2 hours. *(2)*

b) Describe **two** ways that this experiment represents the action of the human gut. *(2)*

(Total = 7 marks)

3 The diagram shows a section through a leaf.

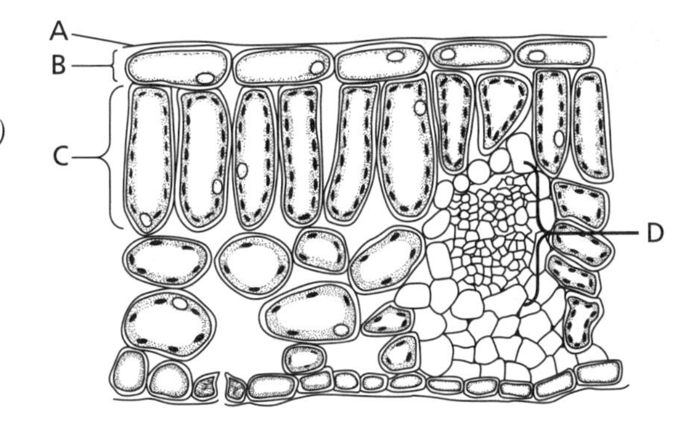

a) Complete the table by naming parts A, B, C and D and giving a function for each. *(4)*

Letter	Name of part	Function of part
A		
B		
C		
D		

b) i) On which surface of this leaf are the stomata found? *(1)*

ii) Draw arrows on the diagram to show the pathway taken by a molecule of carbon dioxide as it passes from the atmosphere to a chloroplast in a palisade mesophyll cell. *(2)*

iii) Explain why this route would change at night. *(2)*

(Total = 9 marks)

4 A student set up the apparatus shown and observed it over 2 hours.

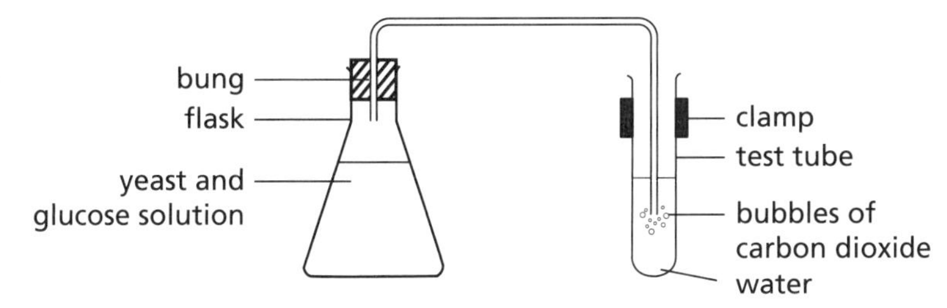

At the beginning, oxygen was available, dissolved in the solution and in the air space. Bubbles of carbon dioxide were produced at a rapid rate.

After 2 hours, there was no oxygen available in the flask. Bubbles of carbon dioxide were observed, but they were produced at a much slower rate.

a) Complete the word equations below to show the processes taking place after 1 hour and after 2 hours, and name each process.

i) After 1 hour *(3)*

.... + O_2 → .... + ... + energy

Name of process: ....

ii) After 2 hours *(3)*

.... → .... + ... + energy

Name of process: ....

b) Both processes release energy. How would the energy released per minute after 1 hour compare with the energy released per minute after 2 hours? *(1)*

(Total = 7 marks)

Extended writing

Example

1 Lipids (fats) are an important source of energy in the human diet. Describe how lipids are digested in the small intestine. *(6)*

Student 1 response
Lipids are fatty foods, like chips. You chew them and swallow them then they reach the small intestine. Bile from the gall bladder is mixed with the food. It acts on the fat in the chips and breaks it down to fatty acids. Digestion means when large molecules are broken down to small ones like fatty acids and these can then be absorbed.
Student 2 response
In the small intestine, pancreatic juice breaks down lipid to fatty acids and glycerol. The enzymes in the small intestine need a neutral pH to work best so bile, which is alkaline, pours onto the food and neutralises the acid from the stomach. Bile also breaks up the fat into tiny droplets to speed up digestion.
Mark scheme
The mark scheme shows how marks are awarded. (1) digestion involves the breakdown of large food molecules to smaller ones (2) (digestion / breakdown) by enzymes (3) lipase (4) (lipase) from pancreas / pancreatic juice / pancreatic duct (5) (breaks down) lipid to fatty acid + glycerol (6) bile (7) from gall bladder / liver (8) (bile) alkaline / neutralises acid from stomach / provides correct pH for lipase action (9) (bile) emulsifies lipids / converts lipids to small droplets / eq (10) so large surface area for lipase to act Total: 6

Student 1 response Total 3/6	Marker comments and tips for success
Lipids are fatty foods, like chips. You chew them and swallow them then they reach the small intestine.	Student 1 has not said enough for any marks. The question asks about what happens in the small intestine, not what happens earlier.
Bile ✔ from the gall bladder ✔ is mixed with the food.	The student gains marks (6) and (7). In questions about the digestive system, marks are often awarded, as here, for the name of the secretion and where it is produced. Remember to include these points.
It acts on the fat in the chips and breaks it down O to fatty acids. O	Bile emulsifies lipid, converting the large globules to smaller droplets. Student 1 does not gain mark (9). Bile does not contain enzymes, so cannot break down lipid to fatty acids and glycerol.
Digestion means when large molecules are broken down to small ones like fatty acids and these can then be absorbed. ✔	The student gains mark (1). It would have been more logical to put this definition of digestion at the beginning. Although no marks are awarded for organisation, planning the answer will help to ensure you do not leave out anything that is important.

Student 2 response Total 5/6	Marker comments and tips for success
In the small intestine, pancreatic juice breaks down lipid ✔	Although lipase is not mentioned, 'breaks down lipid' together with 'pancreatic juice' is just enough for the award of mark (4). Enzymes not mentioned, so mark (2) not awarded.
to fatty acids and glycerol. ✔	The student gains mark (5). Adding the words 'by lipase' would have gained mark (3). In answering questions about enzyme action, like this one, always try to include the name of the enzyme involved and a word equation for the reaction.
The enzymes O in the small intestine need a neutral pH to work best so bile, ✔ which is alkaline, ✔ pours onto the food and neutralises the acid from the stomach.	'Enzymes' is not linked to digestion or breakdown so not enough for mark (2). The student gained mark (6) for 'bile' and mark (8) for 'alkaline'. 'Neutralises acid from the stomach' is another way of getting mark (8).
Bile also breaks up the fat into tiny droplets ✔ to speed up digestion.	'Breaks up the fat into tiny droplets' is equivalent to 'emulsifies lipids' for mark (9). Try to use the correct scientific term, lipid, although you will not usually be penalised for using the word 'fat' instead. A reference to 'large surface area' here would have gained mark (10).

Extended writing questions – general advice

- The mark allocation for extended writing questions is usually 6 marks. This gives a guide as to how long you should spend on this question in relation to the rest of the paper – probably about 6 minutes.
- Use your time sensibly by writing down a brief plan or a list of what you want to include. You can afford to spend 3 minutes on planning and deciding what you are going to write, as 3 minutes will be enough to write an answer that gains full marks. Don't spend too long or you could run out of time for other questions.
- Your plan or list will help to jog your memory so that you remember to include additional relevant points. For questions about enzyme action, like this one, it is always helpful to include the name of the enzyme involved and a word equation for the reaction. Consider whether you should include a comment about the pH for the reaction.
- For questions about the digestive system, marks are often awarded for the name of the secretion and where it is produced so remember to include these points. In this question, marks could be gained for stating where bile is produced or stored and for stating that the enzyme lipase is present in pancreatic juice.
- For further general advice on answering the extended writing questions see pages 72 and 85.

Practice questions

2 Describe how the small intestine is adapted for the absorption of small food molecules produced by digestion. *(6)*

3 Explain how a leaf of a flowering plant is adapted for photosynthesis. *(6)*

4 Describe how a molecule of starch, taken into the mouth in food, becomes a molecule of glycogen in the liver of a human. *(6)*

3 Movement of substances in living organisms

Using and interpreting data

Example

1 Some students investigated the changes that occurred in the air around a plant leaf, in the light and in the dark. The students used the apparatus shown in the diagram. One leaf was enclosed in a clear plastic bag. Inside the bag there were two sensors, each connected to a computer. One sensor detected carbon dioxide concentration and the other sensor detected humidity (the percentage of water in the air). The bag could be sealed to make sure it was airtight. The sensors recorded continuously and the readings were displayed on the computer screen.

healthy plant

bag (around one leaf)

leaf

sensors

computer showing graph with changing composition of air in bag against time

Their first investigation was carried out in the light. The sensors monitored the carbon dioxide and humidity levels inside the bag for 40 minutes. The bag was open for the first 10 minutes, then closed and sealed. At 30 minutes the bag was opened again.

The graph shows the changes in carbon dioxide concentration and humidity recorded by the sensors.

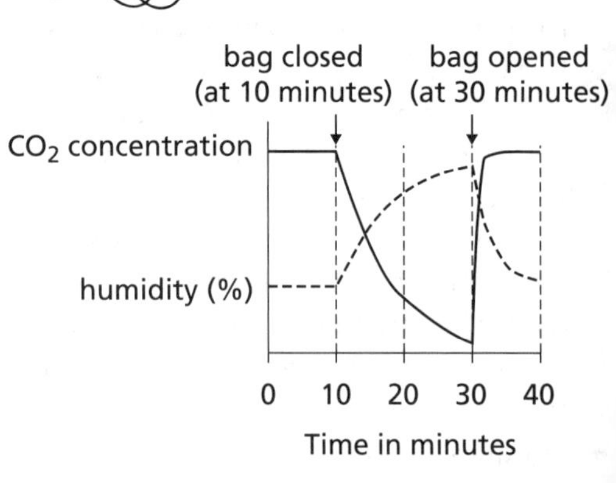

a) Describe the changes that took place in the carbon dioxide concentration inside the bag. Give a reason for each of the changes you describe. Write your answers in the table. One line has been done for you. *(4)*

Time period	Observed change	Reason
0 to 10 minutes	stays the same	carbon dioxide concentration inside the bag is the same as in the air in the room, remains steady
10 to 30 minutes	(1)	(2)
30 to 40 minutes	(3)	(4)

b) Describe and explain the changes in humidity inside the bag, when the bag was closed (between 10 and 30 minutes). *(3)*

c) The students repeated the investigation but this time they completely covered the plant and the sensors with a dark cloth.

i) Copy the axes given for the first graph. Using these axes, draw two line graphs, labelled A and B, to show the changes in carbon dioxide concentration (A) and percentage humidity (B) that you would expect to see from 10 to 30 minutes (when the bag was closed). *(3)*

ii) Give reasons for the changes in carbon dioxide concentration that you show on your graph. *(2)*

(Total = 12 marks)

Student 1 response Total 6/12	Marker comments and tips for success
a) (1) CO_2 level drops ✔ quite quickly.	'Level drops' was enough for the mark in this question. Other questions might require more detailed descriptions [see a) iii)]. Always aim for precise answers, e.g. 'CO_2 level drops, rapidly at first, then more slowly'. It is acceptable to use the formula as shorthand for 'carbon dioxide'.
(2) CO_2 is used up. O	The biological reason is required: photosynthesis is occurring and therefore the carbon dioxide is used up.
(3) The CO_2 level rises rapidly. O	A more precise description is required, including the concentration levelling off, as well as the rapid rise.
(4) The rise in carbon dioxide is due to respiration. O	In light, the rate of photosynthesis is faster than the rate of respiration, so photosynthesis uses up all the carbon dioxide from respiration. The rise must be due to the opening of the bag, which suggests that it is due to carbon dioxide entering from the air outside.
b) The humidity rises. ✔ The water from the leaf evaporates ✔ and is trapped in the bag. ✔	Full marks. Water 'trapped in the bag' is equivalent to 'collects in bag', the last point on the mark scheme.
c) i) 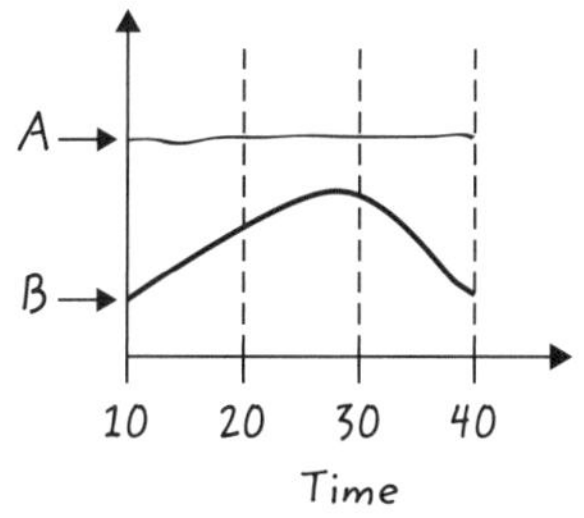 1 = both graphs labelled ✔ 2 = starting position for both graphs O 3 = CO_2 graph shape O 4 = humidity graph shape O	The student has drawn the graphs from time 10 minutes. This is acceptable, as the time period required was from 10 to 30 minutes. The line for A is a little wobbly, but this is acceptable in a sketch graph. The marks are given for the general trend shown. 1 The two graphs A and B were correctly labelled. 2 Student did not start graphs from same positions as before, which were the concentrations in air. 3 Over the 10 to 30 minute time period the CO_2 graph is shown as a horizontal line. Prediction is incorrect as CO_2 level would continue to rise. 4 Over the 10 to 30 minute time period the humidity graph is shown as rising steadily but then falling. The humidity inside the bag would rise steadily and might level off, but it would not fall.
ii) The leaf doesn't photosynthesise in the dark, ✔ so the level of carbon dioxide won't change.	Only 1 mark, as no mention of respiration continuing to take place.

Student 2 response Total 12/12	Marker comments and tips for success
a) (1) CO_2 drops quickly to a very low level. ✔	A good answer, describing how the concentration drops. It is not essential to refer to 'concentration' because this is given on the graph.
(2) The leaf in the bag is photosynthesising and using CO_2 up. ✔	A good answer.
(3) The CO_2 concentration rises quickly to the original level. ✔	'Rises quickly to the original level' is equivalent to 'rise then levels off' in the mark scheme. The answer is both precise and concise.
(4) Carbon dioxide from the air moves into the bag when it is opened. ✔	The concentration of CO_2 at the start, when the bag is open, is the concentration in the air. This suggests that when the concentration rises back to the original level, it is due to air entering the bag.
b) The stomata on the leaf are open ✔ and let out water vapour ✔ by transpiration. ✔	The student did not describe the change in humidity, so does not gain that mark. However, full marks are gained for the clear explanation using biological terms. 'Let out water vapour' is equivalent to 'water passes out of the leaf' in the mark scheme.

(continued)

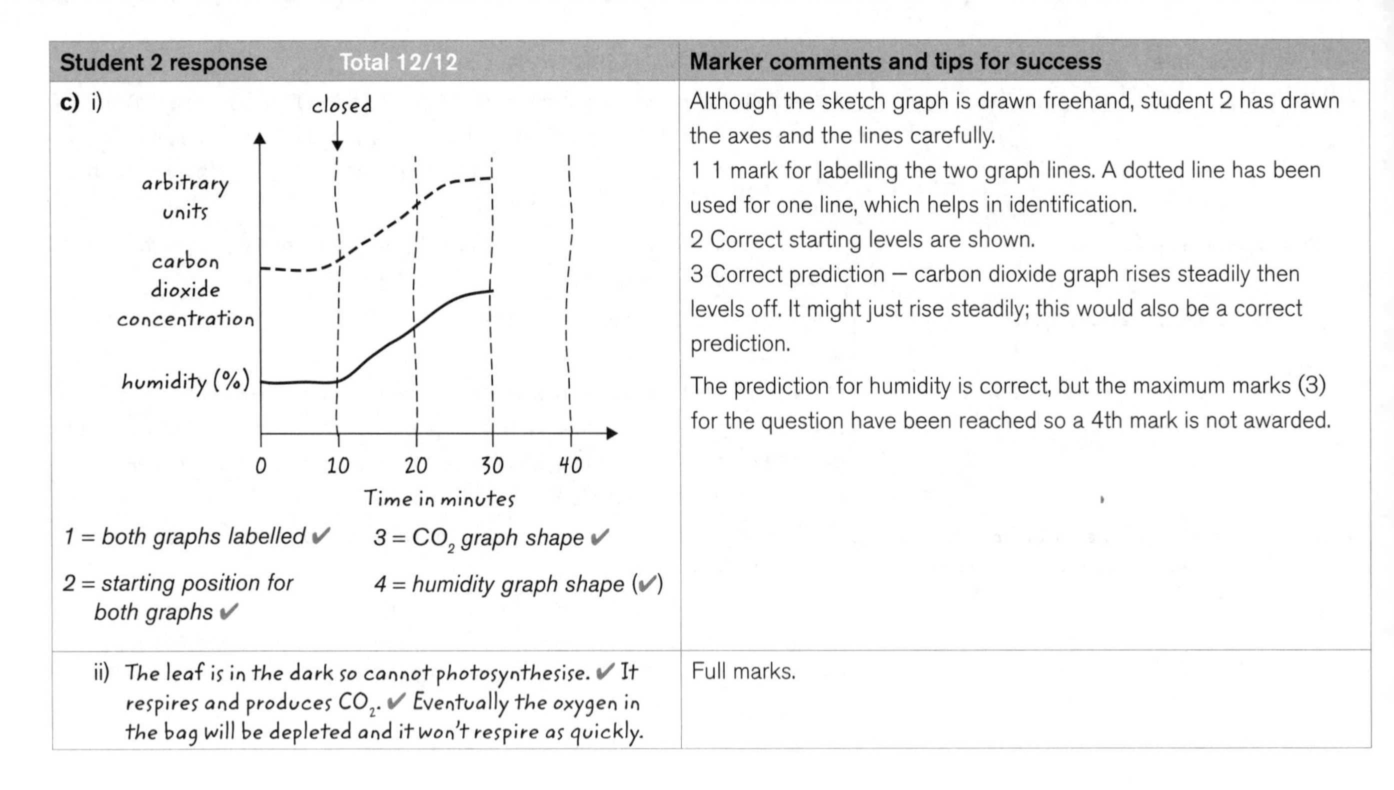

Student 2 response Total 12/12	Marker comments and tips for success
c) i) *1 = both graphs labelled ✔* *2 = starting position for both graphs ✔* *3 = CO_2 graph shape ✔* *4 = humidity graph shape (✔)*	Although the sketch graph is drawn freehand, student 2 has drawn the axes and the lines carefully. 1 1 mark for labelling the two graph lines. A dotted line has been used for one line, which helps in identification. 2 Correct starting levels are shown. 3 Correct prediction – carbon dioxide graph rises steadily then levels off. It might just rise steadily; this would also be a correct prediction. The prediction for humidity is correct, but the maximum marks (3) for the question have been reached so a 4th mark is not awarded.
ii) *The leaf is in the dark so cannot photosynthesise. ✔ It respires and produces CO_2. ✔ Eventually the oxygen in the bag will be depleted and it won't respire as quickly.*	Full marks.

Practice questions

2 'Algal balls' can be made by trapping thousands of single-celled algae in a jelly-like substance. Drops of the jelly mixture are released from a syringe into a liquid to form spherical balls.

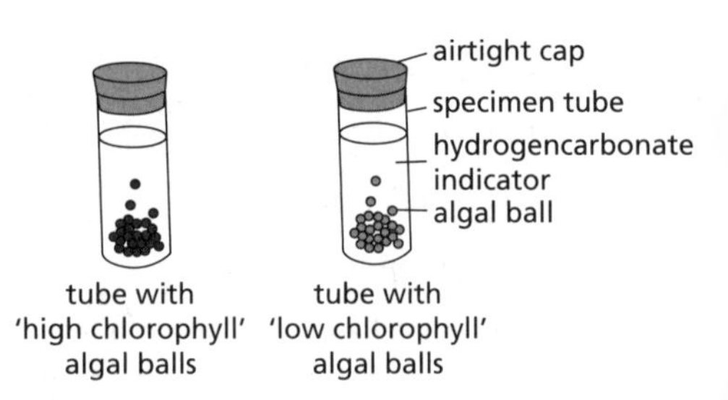

A group of students investigated the effect of chlorophyll concentration on the rate of photosynthesis at different light intensities. They used algal balls that had been made containing different numbers of algae, so they contained different amounts of chlorophyll.

The students prepared five specimen tubes containing 'high chlorophyll' algal balls and five tubes containing the same number of 'low chlorophyll' balls. Each tube contained the same volume of hydrogencarbonate indicator.

They placed pairs of tubes, as shown in the diagram, in five different light intensities. After 60 minutes they used a colorimeter to record the colour of the indicator in each tube. The colour was then converted into a measure of the concentration of carbon dioxide in the solution. This was used as a measure of the rate of photosynthesis. Their results are shown in the graph.

Rate of photosynthesis in arbitrary units: 0.0, 0.1, 0.2, 0.3, 0.4, 0.5, 0.6, 0.7, 0.8, 0.9, 1.0
high chlorophyll
low chlorophyll
Light intensity in arbitrary units: 0.0, 0.5, 1.0, 1.5, 2.0

a) i) Write a word equation to show that carbon dioxide is used in photosynthesis. *(2)*

ii) Explain why the colour of the hydrogencarbonate indicator after 60 minutes can be used to measure the rate of photosynthesis in the tube. *(3)*

b) i) Describe how the rate of photosynthesis for the algal balls with 'high chlorophyll' varies with light intensity. *(3)*

ii) Give **two** differences between the rate of photosynthesis in the 'high chlorophyll' algal balls and the 'low chlorophyll' algal balls. *(2)*

(Total = 10 marks)

3 Many organisations produce information that describes the harmful effects of cigarette smoke and the benefits of stopping smoking. The list below has been extracted from a fact sheet published by an organisation that aims to discourage people from smoking. The information states, for example, that smoking increases the risk of:

- *heart disease, strokes and heart attacks*
- *lung cancer and cancer in other parts of the body*
- *diseases of the chest cavity, including bronchitis and emphysema.*

Graph 1 shows the world cigarette production during the years 1950 to 2000. Graph 2 shows the cigarette consumption per person in the USA (population around 300 million) during part of the same period (1965 to 2000).

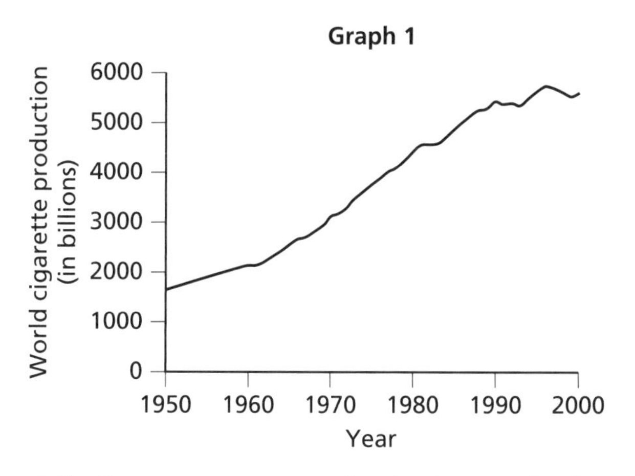

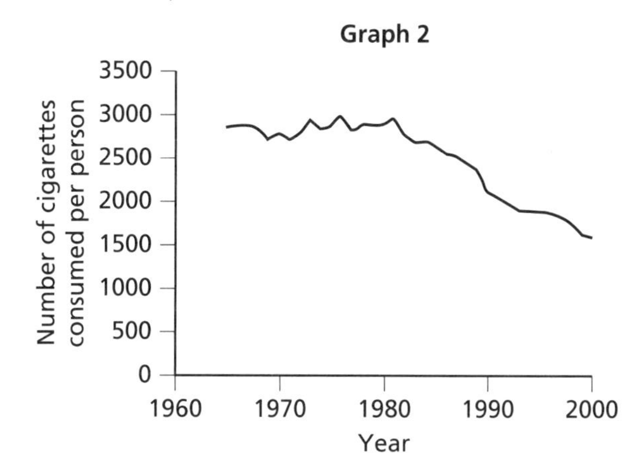

a) i) Suggest **two** reasons for the decrease in cigarette consumption shown in graph 2. *(2)*

ii) Suggest why, in graph 1, the world production of cigarettes increased between 1950 and 2000 even though, in graph 2, the USA showed a decrease in consumption of cigarettes per person during part of this time. *(2)*

b) Bronchitis is an infection of the lungs and is made worse by mucus that collects in the bronchi. Explain why cigarette smoke may lead to an increase in mucus in the bronchi. *(3)*

c) Carbon monoxide is contained in cigarette smoke. Describe and explain the effect this may have on a person who smokes. *(2)*

d) Emphysema is a condition of the lungs in which the alveoli become less elastic and their walls start to break down. Explain why a person with emphysema easily becomes breathless. *(2)*

(Total = 11 marks)

Practical activities

Example

1 An oxygen sensor measures the concentration of oxygen, as a percentage, in a certain volume of air.

The sensor can be used to measure the percentage of oxygen in air exhaled into a plastic bag. The concentration of oxygen in air inhaled from the atmosphere is 21%. The difference between this and the concentration of oxygen in the exhaled air represents the amount of oxygen that has been absorbed from the lungs into the blood.

A student wanted to find out if there is any difference in the percentage of oxygen in exhaled air when she holds her breath for longer and longer periods of time. She used the sensor and wrote down the data she collected.

Student's data

Inhaled and immediately exhaled, O_2 conc. = 17%
Holding breath for 5 seconds, conc. = 14%
After 10 seconds, conc. = 11%
After 30 seconds, conc. = 9%
After 45 seconds, conc. = 7%
After 60 seconds, conc. = 6%

a) i) Draw a suitable table to show all the student's results. Calculate the values for the percentage difference in oxygen concentration between inhaled and exhaled air and include these in the table. *(5)*

ii) Suggest **one** way in which she could have made her results more reliable. *(1)*

iii) Write a conclusion for the student's results. *(1)*

b) i) Name the gas exchange surface in the lungs. *(1)*

ii) Use your knowledge of gas exchange in the lungs to explain the student's results. *(4)*

(Total = 12 marks)

Student 1 response Total 5/12	Marker comments and tips for success
a) i) (table below)	Mark 1 gained for correct number and layout of rows and columns. This orientation is acceptable. Mark 2 lost because no unit of time given in the heading. If 'secs' had been repeated for all values in the column, this would have been acceptable, even though it is clearer to put the unit in the column heading. Mark 3 is for time correctly inserted, but not gained because student 1 put a dash instead of a value (zero) for the first reading. Mark 4 gained for correctly inserting the values for oxygen concentration in the table. Marks 5 and 6 are for calculating the percentage difference in oxygen concentration, but no marks as two errors made.
ii) She could have used a stopwatch. O	An experiment is reliable if similar results are obtained when it is repeated. Using a stopwatch may improve the precision of the time measurement but not the reliability.
iii) If you hold your breath for a long time there is less oxygen in it. O	The student 'wanted to find out if there is any difference in the percentage of oxygen in exhaled air when she holds her breath...'. Your conclusion should therefore summarise the relationship between the time the breath is held and the percentage of oxygen in exhaled air, e.g. 'The longer you hold your breath, the less oxygen there will be in it'.
b) i) The mucus covering the surface of the air sacs. ✓	'Air sacs' is acceptable at this level, but for further study use the correct biological term, 'alveoli'.
ii) With more time, there is longer for the oxygen to move into the bloodstream from the air sacs, ✓ so more oxygen is taken up. ✓	'Taken up' is equivalent to 'absorbed' in the mark scheme. A description of how the oxygen moved (by diffusion, down the concentration gradient) could gain two further marks.

Student 1's table for a) i):

Time breath held O_2	Oxygen in bag (%)	Percentage difference in O_2 conc. ✓1
– O_3	17	4
5 sec	14	7
10 sec	11	10
30	9	12
45	7	15 O_5
60	6 ✓4	16 O_6

<table>
<tr><th>Student 2 response Total 11/12</th><th>Marker comments and tips for success</th></tr>
<tr><td>a) i) ✓1
<table>
<tr><td>Time in seconds</td><td>0</td><td>5</td><td>10</td><td>30</td><td>45 ✓3</td><td>60</td></tr>
<tr><td>Percentage of O_2 in exhaled air</td><td>17</td><td>14</td><td>11</td><td>9</td><td>7</td><td>6 ✓4</td></tr>
<tr><td>Difference in O_2 conc. between exhaled and inhaled air O_2</td><td>4</td><td>7</td><td>10</td><td>12</td><td>14 ✓5</td><td>(✓6)</td></tr>
</table></td><td>Gains maximum 5 marks.
Mark 1 gained for correct layout of rows and columns. This orientation is acceptable.
Mark 2 lost because no unit given (%) for third row.
Mark 3 gained as times are inserted correctly, and 'immediately' correctly interpreted as time 0.
Mark 4 gained for inserting all results for oxygen concentration correctly.
Mark 5 gained for calculating correctly all percentage differences between inhaled air (21%) and exhaled air.
Mark 6 is correct but maximum already reached.</td></tr>
<tr><td>ii) She could repeat the experiment more than once. ✓</td><td>By repeating an experiment several times (usually a minimum of three times) the consistency of the results may be confirmed. Anomalous results may be discarded and the mean calculated.</td></tr>
<tr><td>iii) The longer a person holds their breath, the less oxygen is breathed out in exhaled air. ✓</td><td>A valid conclusion stating the relationship between the two variables (time breath was held and percentage oxygen in exhaled air).</td></tr>
<tr><td>b) i) The bronchioles and the alveoli. O</td><td>The bronchioles do not have a gas exchange surface, so this wrong answer negates the correct answer, alveoli. Be careful and precise when answering.</td></tr>
<tr><td>ii) Oxygen in the inhaled air is at a higher concentration than oxygen in the blood ✓ so it diffuses ✓ into the blood capillaries, through the thin wall of the alveolus. ✓ The longer it stays in the alveolus, the more oxygen diffuses into the blood. ✓</td><td>A good answer, gaining 4 marks.</td></tr>
</table>

Practice questions

2 Some students investigated the distribution of stomata on leaves of ivy. They used a 'variegated' ivy leaf, some parts of which are green and other parts are yellow. The yellow parts contain no chlorophyll.

The students painted clear nail varnish on the lower surface of the leaf and let it dry. They then pressed on some transparent sticky tape and peeled this off with the nail polish. This took an impression of the stomata on the surface of the leaf. They placed the peel on a microscope slide and observed it with a microscope.

They decided to count the number of stomata in the green and yellow parts so that they could make a comparison.

a) i) One student suggested they divide the photomicrograph into four equal sections to make the counting easier. Draw a suitable table that they could use to record their counts in each of the four sections. *(2)*

ii) Divide the photomicrograph into four sections, as suggested by the student, and count the number of stomata in each section. Write your results in the table you have drawn. *(3)*

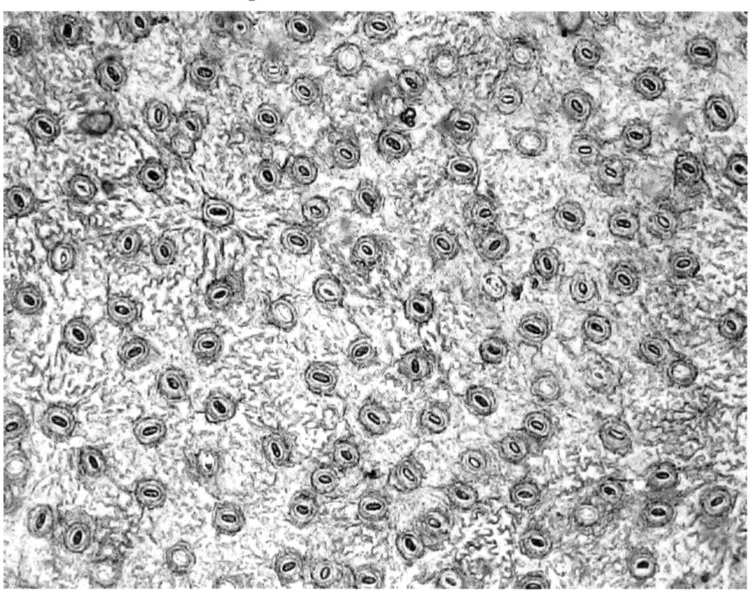

iii) Describe **two** steps you took while doing the counting to make sure the counts were accurate. *(2)*

b) The students then made a similar count of the number of stomata in the peel from a yellow part. The two photomicrographs represented the same area of leaf (6.5 mm × 5.0 mm). The total number of stomata that the students counted from this area on a yellow part of the leaf was 101 stomata.

i) Which part of the leaf had more stomata, the green or the yellow? *(1)*

ii) Another student was not convinced that there was really any difference. Suggest what they should do to be more certain that they had got a result that was correct for these ivy leaves. *(2)*

c) The students also did a peel from the upper surface of the leaf but found no stomata on this surface. Suggest how lack of stomata on the upper surface could be an advantage to the ivy plant. *(2)*

(Total = 12 marks)

3 Single-celled algae, such as *Scenedesmus*, can be mixed with a solution of sodium alginate. If drops of this mixture are released from a dropper (or a syringe) into a solution of calcium chloride, the drops form spherical balls. These are known as algal balls and have a jelly-like texture. Thousands of tiny algae are trapped inside each of the balls. The size of the balls can be varied by using droppers with different-sized tips.

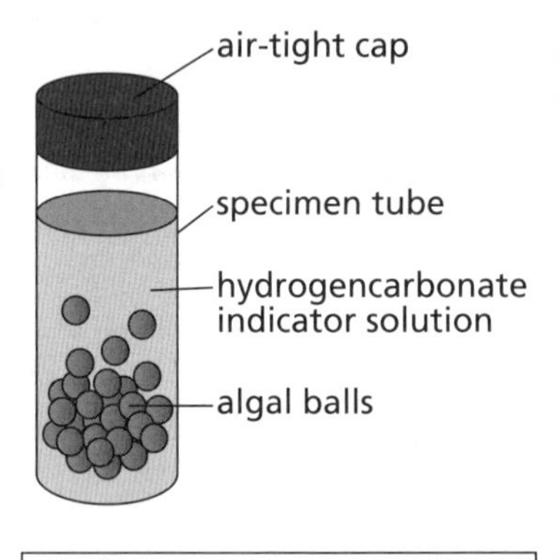

The algae contain chlorophyll and can be used to study processes that occur in green plants, such as photosynthesis and respiration. They can, for example, be set up in tubes as shown in the diagram and used to investigate gas exchange.

A group of students decided to carry out an investigation using algal balls. They wanted to study the effect of different sizes of balls on the rate of gas exchange.

The students were provided with a suspension of algal balls of four different sizes in separate beakers and with a flask of hydrogencarbonate indicator. They had access to standard items of laboratory apparatus, such as measuring cylinders, syringes, beakers and plenty of specimen tubes. The students also had a card that showed the colour of hydrogencarbonate indicator at different concentrations of carbon dioxide.

Hydrogencarbonate indicator can be used to detect changes in carbon dioxide concentration in the solution. When the carbon dioxide concentration is high, the indicator is yellow. As the concentration of carbon dioxide decreases, the colour of the indicator changes to orange-red, then to red, and finally to purple.

a) Describe how you would set up the tubes for the investigation the students want to carry out. *(4)*

b) The students left their apparatus all set up overnight, ready to start in the morning. When they turned on the lights in the laboratory, they noticed that the indicator was yellow in all the tubes. Explain why the indicator was yellow in the tubes. *(2)*

c) They then kept a light on, close to the tubes, and watched as the colour changed in the tubes.

i) What colour changes would you expect? Give a reason for your answer. *(3)*

ii) Describe the measurements you would take to find out if the size of the algal balls has any effect on the rate of gas exchange taking place in the algal balls. Include reference to any practical details and observations you may have to make. *(3)*

iii) Suggest the results that you may obtain and give a reason to support your prediction. *(2)*

(Total = 14 marks)

4 A student did an investigation into transpiration in a plant shoot. She wanted to find out whether the rate of transpiration of a plant shoot was different in the conditions inside a school biology laboratory compared to the conditions outside the laboratory, on the school playing field.

She used the potometer shown in the diagram. She recorded the movement of the liquid in the capillary tube and used this as a measure of the rate of transpiration.

In each place, she recorded the air temperature, humidity of the air and wind speed. Her values are given in table 1.

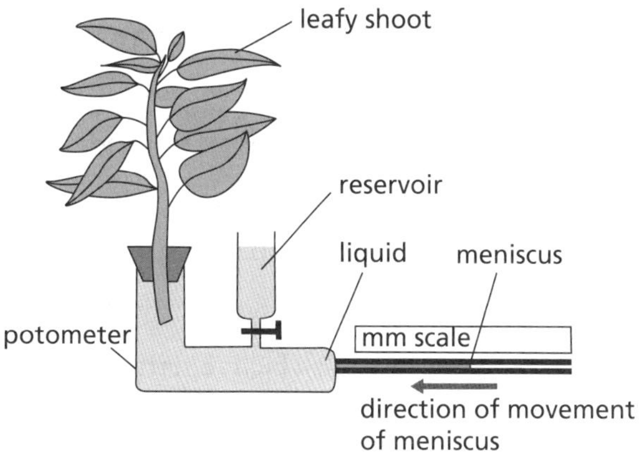

In each place, when she set up the potometer, she waited for 5 minutes. She then started to record the position of the meniscus of the liquid in the capillary tube. The readings she took are given in table 2.

Table 1

Condition	Inside	Outside
Air temperature in °C	23	14
Humidity of air (%)	45	66
Air speed in m per s	0	0.8

Table 2

Time in minutes	Distance moved by meniscus in mm	
	Inside	Outside
1	3	7
2	6	12
3	10	18
4	13	25
5	17	31

She then discussed her investigation and the results she had obtained with other students in the class.

a) She was not sure how to present the results. One student (student A) said it would be best to draw a graph whereas student B asked why she had taken readings each minute and thought she should just take the distance at 5 minutes as the result.

i) What advice would you offer to the student? Give reasons for your answer. *(2)*

ii) What calculation could she do to compare the rate of transpiration in each place, using these results? *(2)*

iii) What assumption did she make in using this as a way of measuring the rate of transpiration? *(1)*

b) The students next looked at conclusions that could be drawn from the results in this investigation. They could see that the total distance moved by the meniscus was more outside, suggesting the rate of transpiration is faster, but they needed more information to help them draw a suitable conclusion. Here are some of the questions they asked. The letters refer to different students asking the questions.

C Why did you leave the potometer for 5 minutes before taking any readings?
D How do you know which of the different factors was influencing the rate of transpiration?
E Did you use the same leafy shoot each time?
F Would differences in light intensity have had an effect on the rate of transpiration in the two places?
G Is it enough just to do the investigation with one shoot and take one set of readings?

After this discussion, the students agreed to work together as a group and investigate factors that affect the rate of transpiration. They decided to use the same apparatus but to bring it into the laboratory and make some modifications to the method. They used the questions listed above to help guide them.

i) What could they do to respond to the question from student D? *(2)*

ii) What could they do to respond to the questions from student E and student G? *(2)*

iii) What answer would you give to student C's question? *(1)*

(Total = 10 marks)

Understanding structure, function and processes

Example

1 a) i) Draw a labelled diagram of a red blood cell. *(2)*

ii) Give **two** ways in which the structure of a white blood cell differs from that of a red blood cell. *(2)*

b) Red blood cells transport oxygen to the cells of the body.

i) Explain how the features of a red blood cell help it carry out this function efficiently. *(3)*

ii) Name the blood vessel in the human body that contains the highest concentration of oxygen. *(1)*

c) White blood cells help reduce infection by pathogens in the body. There are different types of white blood cell. Choose **one** type of white blood cell and describe how it helps reduce the spread of pathogens in the body. *(2)*

(Total = 10 marks)

Student 1 response Total 4/10	Marker comments and tips for success
a) i) nucleus, cytoplasm *drawing* O *label* O	No mark for the drawing. Student 1 has drawn an oval cell, rather than a circular one, or may have attempted to draw a three dimensional view. Biological drawings should show the surface view or sectional view, with no shading. Lines should be used for labels, not arrows. No mark for the labels because the student has mistakenly labelled the shallow centre of the biconcave disc as the nucleus. This error negates the mark for labelling the cytoplasm correctly.
ii) *A white blood cell hasn't got haemoglobin so it's white, not red.* O *It's much larger than a red blood cell.* ✔	The question asks for **two** differences in structure, but because haemoglobin and colour are not 'structures', no marks are gained for the first statement. There are often several possible answers to select from, so think carefully about what you write. Size is a valid difference in structure so gains a mark.
b) i) *It transports oxygen* O *and is a biconcave shape.* O	No mark for 'transports oxygen' because the student did not link the function to the feature – the haemoglobin. The student had already mentioned haemoglobin in the answer to a) ii) but marks cannot be awarded across question parts. No mark for 'biconcave' because the student did not explain how the shape helps the red cell to function efficiently. In this 'explain' question the features have to be linked to their function to gain marks.
ii) *The pulmonary vein* ✔	This vein carries freshly oxygenated blood from the lungs to the heart.
c) *Lymphocytes make antibodies* ✔ *that can attach to bacteria* ✔ *and clump them together.*	Student 1 gains full marks for naming lymphocytes and describing their action.

Student 2 response Total 8/10	Marker comments and tips for success
a) i) cell membrane; haemoglobin *drawing ✔ label ✔*	Drawing shows circular shape and central hollow (mark 1). Cell membrane labelled (mark 2). Mark scheme does not reward drawing quality, but note neat drawing and labelling, with label line just touching the membrane. Haemoglobin is not a cell structure (it is part of the cytoplasm).
ii) *A white blood cell has got a nucleus. ✔ It has no haemoglobin. The lymphocytes are an oval shape ✔ and other white blood cells have an irregular shape.*	One mark for nucleus and one for 'oval shape', which is acceptable for the shape. The statement about 'irregular shape' is an alternative way of gaining the same mark. No mark for 'no haemoglobin' because it is a substance in the cytoplasm, not a structure.
b) i) *The haemoglobin ✔ can carry oxygen ✔ from the lungs to the muscles. Its shape means that it has a large surface area to volume ratio O so oxygen from the lungs can diffuse in quickly. ✔*	Full marks given. No mark for the correct description of the large SA to volume ratio because the feature, the biconcave shape, was not described. However, linking the SA to volume ratio with rapid diffusion of oxygen was considered to be worth the final mark. The shape needs to be described as biconcave (or similar) to gain the shape mark.
ii) *The aorta O*	The pulmonary vein has the highest oxygen concentration.
c) *A white blood cell engulfs bacteria O and destroys them. ✔*	Student 2 ignored the instruction to 'choose one type of white blood cell' and did not name the 'phagocyte' as the type that engulfs bacteria. However, 1 mark was given for 'destroy bacteria'. Any appropriate example of a pathogen would be acceptable.

Practice questions

2 The diagram shows the human lungs in the chest cavity. Some of the structures are labelled with the letters A to H. Use letters on the diagram in your answers to the questions that follow.

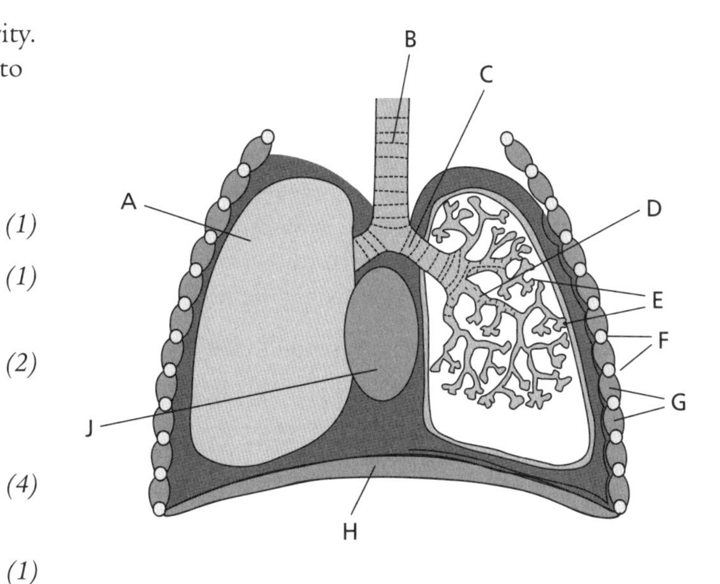

a) i) Give the letter of the structure that is strengthened by C-shaped rings of cartilage. *(1)*

ii) Describe why these rings are necessary. *(1)*

b) i) Give the letters of **two** structures that move causing air to be taken into the lungs. *(2)*

ii) For each structure named in b) i), describe how contraction of muscles results in air being inhaled. *(4)*

c) i) Give the letter of the surface in the lungs where gas exchange takes place. *(1)*

ii) Describe **two** ways that this structure is adapted for gas exchange. *(2)*

(Total = 11 marks)

3 Water is taken in by the roots of flowering plants. The water then travels up the stem and passes out from the leaves.

a) i) Name the cells in the root that take up water from the surrounding soil. *(1)*

ii) Name the process by which water enters these root cells. *(1)*

iii) What features do these root cells have that adapt them for uptake of water? *(2)*

b) Water travels up the stem of a plant in the xylem.

i) Describe how features of the cells in the xylem helps the water to travel up the stem. *(2)*

ii) What feature of the cells in the xylem helps to provide support for the plant? *(1)*

c) i) Name the process by which water passes out from the leaves. *(1)*

ii) Name the pores through which water vapour passes out from the leaves. *(1)*

iii) These pores can open and close in different conditions. Describe how these changes are brought about. *(3)*

(Total = 12 marks)

4 a) i) Name the process by which water is lost from the leaf of a plant. *(1)*

ii) Explain why a plant takes up less water on a day that is humid (damp) and the air is still, compared with a day that is dry and windy. *(4)*

b) The diagram shows a section through a leaf of marram grass. This grass grows in sandy places, where the water drains away quickly. It shows adaptations that help it live in dry places. In dry conditions, the leaf rolls up as shown in the diagram.

Suggest how features of the leaf help reduce water loss. In your answer, include features of the outside (top) surface and features shown on the inner (lower) side of the leaf. *(4)*

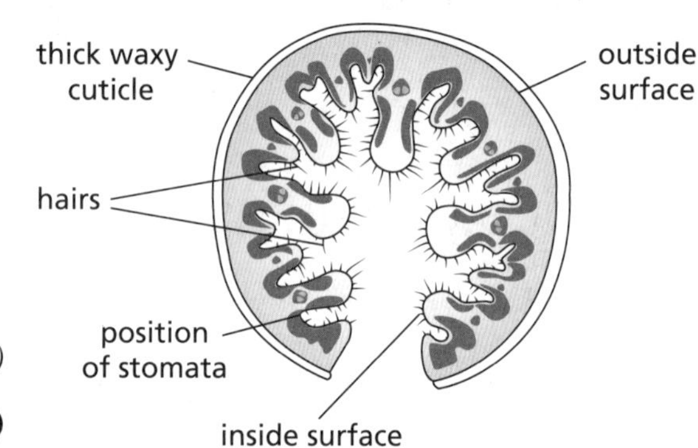

(Total = 9 marks)

5 The diagram shows a simplified view of the human heart and some of the blood vessels in the blood circulatory system. Some of the structures are labelled with the letters A to L. Arrows show the direction of blood flow. Use letters on the diagram in your answers to the questions that follow.

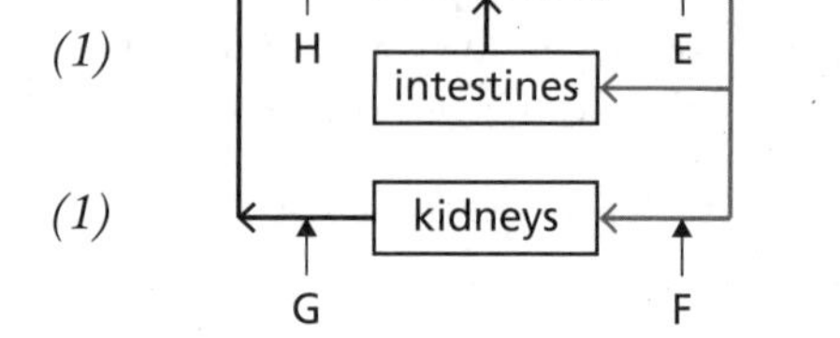

a) Name the structure represented by A. *(1)*

b) i) Name the part of the heart shown by letter C. *(1)*

ii) Explain why the walls of part J and part C are of different thickness. *(2)*

c) i) Give the letter of the vein that carries oxygenated blood. *(1)*

ii) Explain why most veins carry deoxygenated blood. *(2)*

d) Suggest why the hepatic portal vein carries high concentrations of glucose and amino acids. *(2)*

e) i) Give the letter of the blood vessel with the highest blood pressure. *(1)*

ii) Explain why it is important that this blood vessel carries blood at high pressure. *(1)*

f) Explain why there is a difference in the concentration of urea in the blood carried in vessels F and G. *(2)*

g) i) Give the letter of **one** blood vessel that contains valves. *(1)*

ii) What is the function of valves? *(1)*

(Total = 15 marks)

Applying principles

Example

1 A glucometer is an instrument that measures the concentration of glucose in the blood.

The test uses a paper strip that contains an enzyme called glucose oxidase. When a drop of blood is added to the paper strip, the enzyme converts glucose to gluconic acid. This generates an electric current that the glucometer measures and translates into a numerical value.

a) i) In which part of the blood is glucose transported? *(1)*

ii) There are thousands of different chemical substances in the blood. Suggest why it is only glucose that reacts with the enzyme in the paper strip. *(2)*

b) Give **two** processes in the body that can lead to a change in the glucose level in the blood. State whether the change is an increase or a decrease. In each case, name or describe the blood vessel in which the change might be detected. Write your answers in the table below. *(4)*

Description of process	Increase or decrease in blood glucose level	Blood vessel(s) involved

c) Some people have diabetes and are not able to produce enough insulin. Diabetics often find it useful to use a glucometer to monitor their blood glucose so that they can take action if necessary.

i) Where is insulin produced in the body? *(1)*

ii) How does insulin help reduce the level of glucose in the blood? *(2)*

d) The enzymes used in a glucometer are obtained from cultures of microorganisms. Suggest how the enzymes are produced on a large scale from these microorganisms. *(2)*

(Total = 12 marks)

Student 1 response Total 5/12	Marker comments and tips for success
a) i) In the capillaries ○	Capillaries are not part of the blood.
ii) Each enzyme breaks down only one thing e.g. amylase breaks down starch. ✓	Equivalent to enzyme works with only one substrate. Giving an example helps to illustrate what you mean. Enzyme action could be mentioned in questions on almost any topic, so make sure you understand how enzymes work and use enzyme terminology. Only 1 mark as no mention of active site.
b) Action of insulin — decrease. ✓ Hepatic vein ✓	The answer should state how the glucose is affected by insulin, e.g. conversion to glycogen. However, as the student gave 'decrease' correctly, this just gained the mark. Insulin acts on glucose in the liver, and the decrease could be detected in the hepatic vein.
Respiration in the muscles — decrease. ✓ Blood vessel from muscles ○	Respiration takes place in all living cells, so any named organ or group of cells would be correct here. You are not expected to know the names of blood vessels from muscles, so if the student had put 'vein' from muscle instead of vessel this would have gained the mark.

(continued)

Student 1 response Total 5/12	Marker comments and tips for success
c) i) *In the small intestine* O	Incorrect. Insulin is produced in the pancreas.
ii) *It acts on the muscles, which take it up from the blood.* ✔	The mark allocation (2) should have suggested to the student that more than one statement about the action of insulin was needed. Insulin also stimulates the conversion of glucose to glycogen.
d) *Large numbers of microorganisms are grown in a jelly. They are crushed and the enzyme is extracted.* O	You are expected to know about large-scale production of useful compounds from microorganisms, and here you are expected to apply your knowledge to a similar yet unfamiliar situation. A reference to fermenters was needed.

Student 2 response Total 10/12	Marker comments and tips for success
a) i) *In the liquid between the blood cells* O	You are expected to know the correct name for the plasma.
ii) *The glucose molecules are the only ones that fit* ✔ *onto the active site* ✔ *of the enzyme on the strip.*	Full marks for this well-expressed answer.
b) *Glucose converted to glycogen in the liver with insulin helping – decrease.* ✔ *Hepatic vein* ✔	Full marks.
Respiration in the kidneys – decrease ✔ *Renal vein* ✔	Respiration takes place in all living cells, so any named organ or group of cells would be correct here. The student has thought about the blood vessels they know and has chosen respiration in the kidneys so that 'renal vein' can be given as the blood vessel involved.
c) i) *In the pancreas* ✔	Correct.
ii) *It causes the liver cells to take up more glucose.* ✔	For b) the student said, correctly, that glucose was also converted to glycogen in the liver, with the help of insulin. However, the examiner cannot give marks to answers in another part of the question. To get the second mark, this same answer has to be repeated.
d) *An industrial fermenter* ✔ *could be used. The microorganisms are kept at the right temperature* ✔ *and provided with nutrient liquid and oxygen. The enzymes are separated from the liquid at the end.* (✔)	The student successfully applied knowledge of fermenters to the production of enzymes. The last statement would also have gained a mark but the maximum for part d) had been reached.

Practice questions

2 A scientist was preparing to give a lecture to some students. As they entered the fairly small room they saw a computer trace was being projected onto the wall. The trace showed the concentration of carbon dioxide gas in the air of the room. As more students came in, they watched as the concentration of carbon dioxide continued to rise.

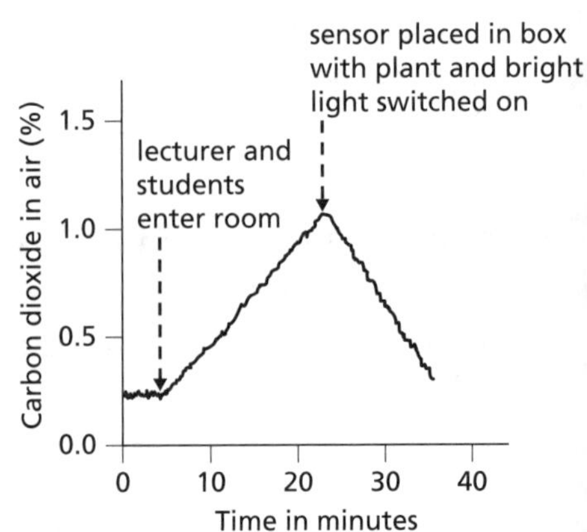

One of the students asked what was happening. The scientist pointed to a sensor lying on the table. This sensor measured the concentration of carbon dioxide in the air in the room. The scientist had previously closed the windows of the room to reduce movement of air between the room and outside.

On the table beside the scientist he had a large, open, transparent box containing a potted plant. He placed the sensor inside the box, and then sealed the air inside it by placing a lid on the box. He switched on a bright light, which he pointed towards the box. The line on the wall began to fall steadily.

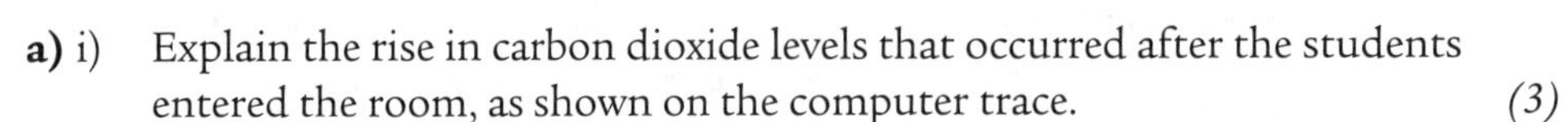

a) i) Explain the rise in carbon dioxide levels that occurred after the students entered the room, as shown on the computer trace. *(3)*

ii) Explain the fall in carbon dioxide levels inside the box containing the plant when the scientist switched on a bright light. *(3)*

iii) Suggest what would happen to the levels of carbon dioxide inside the box if the scientist put a light-proof sheet around the box, preventing light from entering it. Give reasons for your answer. *(2)*

b) The scientist asked the students to suggest what would happen if he took the sensor into a field of maize (corn) so that he could monitor changes in carbon dioxide over a 24-hour period. He told the students to divide the 24 hours into four blocks of six hours, as listed:

- midnight to 06.00 hrs
- 06.00 hrs to 12 noon
- 12 noon to 18.00 hrs
- 18.00 hrs to midnight

i) Sketch a graph to show the changes you would expect for carbon dioxide concentration in the field of maize over a 24-hour period. *(3)*

ii) Give a reason for the changes in carbon dioxide concentration you show on your graph for each of these time periods. *(4)*

(Total = 15 marks)

3 A group of students went on a trek in a high mountain area. They travelled by plane to a starting point at an altitude of 3000 m. They then walked for about 10 days, mostly around 4000 m with some passes at over 5000 m.

At first they noticed that their breathing rate seemed faster than usual and they felt quite breathless. They didn't walk far before stopping for a rest. After a few days they felt much better and were able to keep walking at their usual pace. The students realised they were suffering from the effects of lower levels of oxygen in the atmosphere at high altitude.

a) At sea level, the percentage of oxygen in air is about 21% but at 4000 m the percentage of oxygen is only about 13% of the air.

i) Name the gas exchange surface in the lungs. *(1)*

ii) Explain how the lower level of oxygen in the air breathed in would affect the rate of oxygen uptake into the blood. *(2)*

iii) How does a faster rate of breathing help the students overcome the shortage of oxygen? *(2)*

b) A doctor travelling with the group was able to measure the haemoglobin content of the blood for some students. After 3 or 4 days, the students who were tested showed an increase in haemoglobin concentration. This increase was maintained for several weeks after the students had returned home, to lower altitudes.

When they were home again, they did some research and found some typical values for haemoglobin concentration (in males) at different altitudes. These are shown in the table.

Altitude	Haemoglobin concentration in g per dm^3
at sea level	148
visitor to Mount Everest at 5790 m	196

i) Explain why an increase in haemoglobin concentration helps visitors to high altitudes. *(2)*

ii) Suggest why the students were pleased that the data they found in their research agreed with their own measurements made on their mountain trek. *(1)*

c) Suggest why some athletes undertake training at high altitude in the period leading up to an important athletic event, such as running a marathon. *(2)*

(Total = 10 marks)

4 Coordination and control

Practical activities

Example

1 Woodlice are small invertebrate animals that often live under logs or stones.

Some students set up an investigation into responses of woodlice to humidity. The students used a choice chamber, as shown in the diagram. They used wet cotton wool to provide moist air in one half of the choice chamber and calcium chloride pellets to provide dry air in the other half. A cover was placed over the choice chamber to keep it in the dark.

The students put 10 woodlice into the choice chamber through the hole at the top. They then observed the distribution of the woodlice in the two halves of the choice chamber at 1 minute intervals for 10 minutes. The cover was removed when observations were made.

Their observations are given in the table.

diagram to show parts of choice chamber

lid with hole for adding small animals

gauze sheet across which the animals can move freely

base divided by plastic walls into two sectors

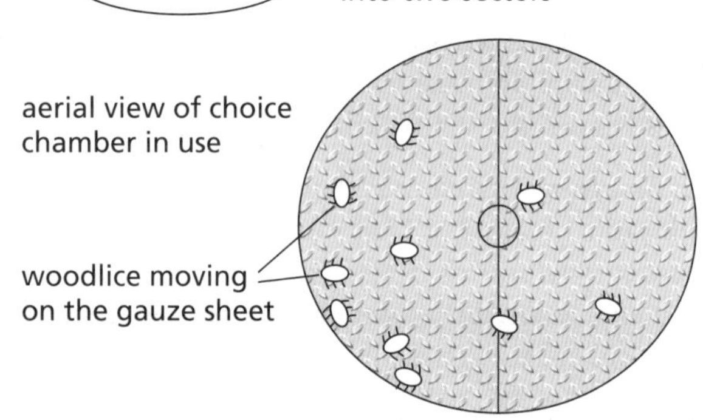

Time in minutes	Number of woodlice	
	Moist air	**Dry air**
1	3	7
2	7	3
3	5	5
4	8	2
5	6	4
6	10	0
7	6	4
8	8	2
9	6	4
10	7	3
Total number of woodlice recorded in 10 minutes	66	

a) Complete the table to show the total number of woodlice counted in the half of the choice chamber with dry air during the whole investigation (in 10 minutes). *(1)*

b) i) Describe the pattern of distribution of woodlice during the first 5 minutes. *(2)*

ii) Suggest why the students continued to make observations for 10 minutes. Use results from the experiment to support your answer. *(2)*

iii) Write a conclusion for this investigation in terms of preferences shown by the woodlice. *(2)*

c) i) Suggest how you could adapt this method to investigate the responses of woodlice to light and dark. *(3)*

ii) With reference to the habitat of woodlice, predict the preferences they might show. Give a reason for your answer. *(2)*

(Total = 12 marks)

Student 1 response Total 8/12	Marker comments and tips for success
a) 34 ✔	This result shows that after 10 minutes the woodlice have been found on the moist side almost twice as often as on the dry side, information that helps in answering subsequent parts of the question.
b) i) *Sometimes they are mostly in the moist air, then they move, so there can be 5 each side, or more in the dry air.* ✔	The description of the variable pattern, gains 1 mark. From the mark allocation (2) the student should expect another point and look more carefully at the data. The change to more woodlice staying in the moist half begins at 4 minutes.
ii) *The woodlice needed time to explore and find conditions they liked best.* ✔ *After 4 minutes all the results show more in the moist air.* ✔	The first statement is equivalent to 'time to settle' in the mark scheme. The second statement, by referring correctly to the data, earns the second mark.
iii) *The woodlice spend more time in the moist air than in dry air,* ✔ *they seem to prefer moist air.* ✔	The student has concluded that the woodlice prefer moist air, and referred to the choice being between moist air and dry air.
c) i) *I would cover one half of the top with tape so the space below was dark.* ✔ *I would use the same number of woodlice* ✔ *and count the number in the light every minute.*	When asked to design an experiment, remember to say how you keep all the conditions (variables) constant, except for the one you are testing. Saying that the temperature was kept the same, or taking the hint in the question and suggesting damp cotton wool in the base, would have gained the third mark.
ii) *Woodlice like the light.* O	You are only expected to know about the organisms listed in the specification. If asked about an unfamiliar animal, you can use information in the question and your knowledge of biological principles to answer. So check the question text and underline key points. The habitat of woodlice is stated in the first line of the question.

Student 2 response Total 11/12	Marker comments and tips for success
a) 34 ✔	You should read all parts of a data-based question before starting so that you can understand the nature of the information. Very often, the answer to one part helps you to answer another.
b) i) *I don't think there is a pattern* ✔ *because first there are 7 on one side and 3 on the other, then the opposite. After 3 minutes there are more on the moist side.* ✔	2 marks gained, one for recognising that there is no pattern in the first few minutes, the second for observing that there seem to be more woodlice on the moist side in minutes 4 and 5.
ii) *You get more reliable results by repeating an experiment,* ✔ *so it is better to repeat it 10 times. The results at 1 minute are anomalous because more are in the dry air.* ✔	More reliable results by 'repeating an experiment' was allowed as equivalent to 'repetition of observations' on the mark scheme. The second mark is for a correct reference to the data at 1 minute.
iii) *More woodlice prefer the moist side of the chamber.* ✔	From the results, woodlice prefer moist air to dry air. The student's conclusion is incomplete because it refers only to moist air and does not state what the other choice was.
c) i) *I would cover half the lid with something dark* ✔ *and leave the base empty.* ✔ *I would make sure that all other conditions, such as temperature, remained constant.* ✔	The results of the first experiment showed that woodlice preferred moist air, so to find their preference for light or dark the base should be left empty or filled with moist cotton wool to keep the humidity constant.
ii) *Woodlice live under logs and stones, where there is shade,* ✔ *so I predict that they prefer the dark.* ✔	A good answer. The student read the information in the first line about the woodlice living under logs and stones so was able to infer that they would prefer to be in the dark rather than the light.

Practice questions

2 Some students investigated responses of cress seedlings to different sources of light.

The students sowed some cress seeds in specimen tubes on damp cotton wool. They then wrapped each tube with a light-proof cover of aluminium foil, except for a small window on one side. They covered this window with transparent plastic film of different colours. This meant the growing seedlings received light of different colours. For tube A, they used a black cover over the window so that the seedlings did not receive any light.

They left the tubes by a window. After 4 days the students removed the covers and made observations of the growth of the seedlings. The appearance of the seedlings was as shown in the diagrams of tubes A to E.

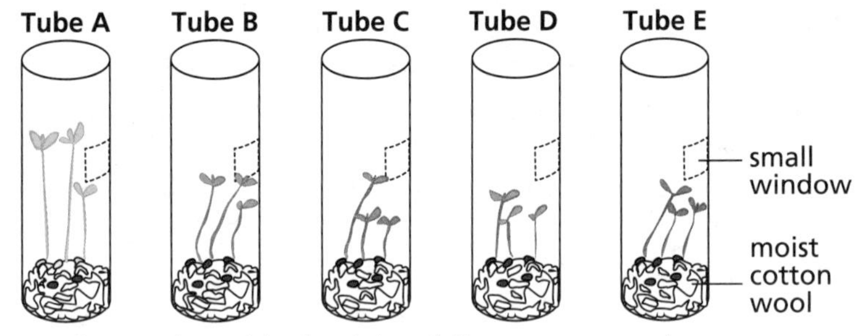

specimen tubes with aluminium foil covers removed

The table below summarises the colours of light for the growing seedlings. The students also used this table to record their results.

Tube	Colour of light	Height of seedlings in cm			Description of angle of growth and colour of seedlings
A	dark (no light)				
B	white (normal light)				seedlings green, growth towards the light (bend from vertical)
C	red				
D	green	0.8	0.6	0.6	seedlings green, growth upright
E	blue				

a) i) Copy the table and record the heights of the three seedlings in each of the tubes. Write your measurements in the correct spaces in the table. Measurements for tube D have been done for you. *(4)*

ii) Describe how you made your measurements of height to ensure they are accurate and comparable in all the tubes. *(2)*

iii) Describe the appearance of the seedlings giving the direction of growth and colour of seedlings. Descriptions for seedlings in tubes B and D have been done for you. *(3)*

b) Seedlings in tube A grew the tallest. Suggest what would happen to the seedlings in this tube if the investigation was continued for several more days. Give a reason for your answer. *(2)*

c) Explain why the seedlings in tube B grew towards the light. *(2)*

d) How could you set up the experiment to make the results more reliable? *(1)*

(Total = 14 marks)

3 Two students carried out an investigation into their reaction times. They used an electronic clock as a timer. The clock was accurate to 0.01 seconds.

Student A started the clock by using a switch hidden below the table so that student B could not see when it was being started.

As soon as the clock started running, student B had to stop it by pressing a button. The time on the clock showed the reaction time in seconds. They repeated this 10 times.

Here are student B's results, as recorded from the figures read from the clock.

0.11 0.13 0.14 0.12 0.18 0.15 0.13 0.15 0.16 0.15

The students then changed places so that student B started the clock and student A had to stop it. Here are student A's results.

0.12 0.10 0.26 0.16 0.15 0.11 0.14 0.10 0.13 0.16

a) i) Organise the results for both students in a suitable table to present the results. *(3)*

ii) Identify any anomalous results. *(1)*

iii) Calculate the mean value for the reaction time for student B. Show your working. *(2)*

b) Outline the pathway taken by nerve impulses in the body from the stimulus (seeing clock has been started) until the finger presses on the button. Include the names of the neurones in the pathway. *(4)*

c) The students decided to use the same method to find out whether listening to music through earphones affected their reaction times. Describe the steps they would take to do this. *(3)*

(Total = 13 marks)

4 Some bean seeds were soaked in water and then pinned to a cork disc that had a layer of damp cotton wool pinned to its surface. The disc was held vertically and after 5 days the bean seedlings had grown as shown in diagram A.

Diagram A

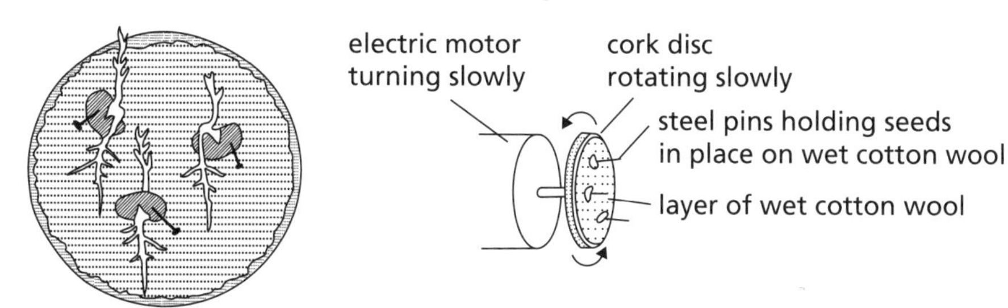

a) i) On the diagram, label the shoot (plumule) and the root (radicle). *(2)*

ii) Describe the response to gravity, as shown by the root. *(2)*

b) The disc with seeds can be attached to a klinostat, as shown in diagram B. This apparatus can be used to investigate the responses of roots and shoots to gravity. When the disc rotates, for the growing shoots and roots, the direction of gravity is continually changing.

In an investigation, the disc was rotated slowly, at a speed that just eliminated the effect of gravity. Describe the predicted direction of growth of the shoots and roots of the seeds pinned to the cork, when the disc is rotating. *(2)*

c) You are asked to use the same set up as shown in diagram A and investigate the response of the shoots to light from one side. You are provided with seedlings at the stage shown in diagram A.

i) Describe how you would set up your investigation. *(3)*

ii) Draw a diagram of the shoots to show your expected results after 3 days. *(2)*

(Total = 11 marks)

Understanding structure, function and processes

Example

1 a) The diagram shows a kidney nephron and its blood vessels.

Blood is filtered in the capsule and glomerulus part of the tubule.

i) Name the artery that carries blood from the aorta to part A. *(1)*

ii) The artery bringing blood to A is wider than the blood vessel leaving the capsule and between the two vessels the blood travels through a network of capillaries. Suggest how this helps the filtration process. *(2)*

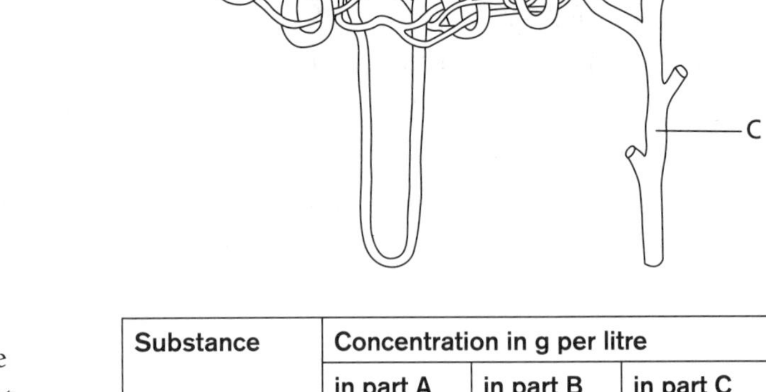

b) The table shows the concentrations of proteins, urea and glucose in the liquid in parts A, B and C. For each substance below, describe and explain the changes in concentration measured in the different parts of the nephron.

i) Protein *(2)*

ii) Glucose *(2)*

iii) Urea *(2)*

Substance	Concentration in g per litre		
	in part A	in part B	in part C
protein	75.0	0.0	0.0
glucose	1.0	1.0	0.0
urea	3.0	3.0	21.0

c) The data given in the table are for a healthy person on an average day. Describe and explain the changes you would expect in the composition of the liquid in part C in the following cases.

i) The person ate a meal containing a very large amount of meat. *(2)*

ii) The person took in the same amount of food and drink on a very cold day. *(2)*

(Total = 13 marks)

Student 1 response Total 9/13	Marker comments and tips for success
a) i) *Hepatic artery* O	
ii) *Ultrafiltration* ✔ *is happening. This is filtration under high pressure* ✔ *caused by the blood vessel leaving the capsule being narrower.*	Full marks.
b) i) *There is a high concentration of protein in the blood at A but none in the capsule or collecting duct.* ✔ *The protein can't leave the blood, it is important for growth.* O	Student 1 refers to the 'capsule' and 'collecting duct' instead of B and C. It is safer to use the letters here in case you give the wrong name. Explanations should describe a mechanism that causes the results shown.
ii) *Glucose is found in A and B but not in the collecting duct.* O *It goes into the capsule from the blood* O *then is absorbed back into the blood at the proximal convoluted tubule.* ✔	Student 1 did not describe the equal concentration in A and B and in the second statement, there is no reference to the small size of glucose molecules. 'Absorbed back into the blood', is equivalent to 'reabsorbed'.

(continued)

Student 1 response Total 9/13	Marker comments and tips for success
iii) Urea is found in A, B and C but there is a lot more in C. ✔ More urea is passed into the urine so it can be excreted. O	The second statement is incorrect. The increase in the concentration of urea is due to water being reabsorbed from the filtrate.
c) i) Meat contains a lot of protein, which is digested to amino acids. The amino acids are broken down to urea ✔ in the liver and so the urine would contain more urea. ✔	Full marks.
ii) The person won't sweat as much ✔ so more water will be lost in the urine. ✔	If body processes are to work well it is important that the water content of the blood is kept constant (osmoregulation). If the water content of the blood increases, the hormone ADH is produced and acts on the collecting duct, causing more water to be excreted in the urine.

Student 2 response Total 10/13	Marker comments and tips for success
a) i) Renal artery ✔	
ii) The blood is under high pressure. ✔ The small molecules like urea are filtered through the capillary walls O into the capsule.	The high blood pressure increases the rate of filtration. If the student had mentioned the term 'ultrafiltration' this would also have been worth a mark.
b) i) There is a lot of protein in A but none in B or C. ✔ The protein molecules are too large to pass through into B. ✔	Try to use correct scientific terms, such as 'high concentration' rather than 'a lot of', although examiners give credit where possible.
ii) Glucose concentration is the same in B as in A, but there is none in C. ✔ The glucose is reabsorbed ✔ in the first coiled tubule.	'First coiled tubule' is equivalent to 'proximal convoluted tubule'. Although there are several acceptable names for the parts of the kidney, it is better to use the name in the specification.
iii) The small urea molecules pass from the blood into B. ✔ Later the concentration increases in the collecting duct C. O This is due to water being reabsorbed. ✔	No mark for the second sentence, as no statement that concentrations in A and B are the same. The student had described this correctly for glucose, but needed to repeat it for urea. Each question part is marked separately, so, if relevant, you must repeat phrases to give full answers.
c) i) Meat contains carbohydrate, so the urine would contain more sugar. O	Although meat does contain carbohydrate (glycogen), which will be digested to glucose, none of it will appear in the urine because all glucose in the kidney filtrate is reabsorbed into the blood in the proximal convoluted tubule.
ii) The urine would be more dilute. ✔ In cold weather less water is lost as sweat, so more will be lost in urine ✔ to keep the concentration of the blood constant.	Full marks.

Practice questions

2 The diagram shows the structure of the human eye.

a) The table lists the functions of some parts of the eye. Use letters from the diagram to complete the table, matching the parts of the eye to their functions. Write one letter only in each box. *(4)*

Function	Letter of part
controls the amount of light entering the eye	
carries nerve impulses to the brain	
controls the thickness of the lens	
bends (refracts) light rays	
has receptors for light	

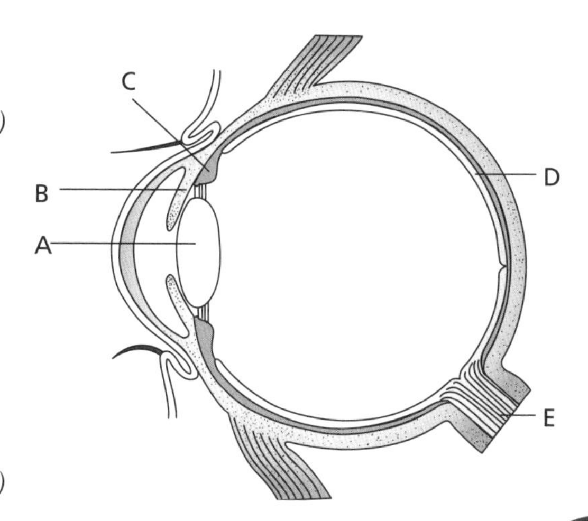

b) i) Mark the position of the **blind spot** with an arrow and the letter **X**. *(1)*

ii) Explain why an image falling on the blind spot cannot be seen. *(2)*

c) A girl was watching athletics in a large stadium. She then looked down at the watch on her wrist. Describe the changes that take place in parts A and C of the eye to bring the image of the watch to a focus on the retina. *(3)*

(Total = 10 marks)

3 a) The table shows the names of some hormones, the organs that produce them and one effect of each hormone on the body. Complete the table by filling in the empty boxes. The first row has been done for you. *(6)*

Name of hormone	Organ that secretes hormone	One effect of the hormone on the body
adrenaline	adrenal gland	increases heart rate
	pancreas	
		growth and development of the male sexual organs
progesterone		

b) Hormonal coordination occurs by the transmission of chemical substances through the bloodstream. How is nervous coordination achieved? *(2)*

(Total = 8 marks)

4 a) What is meant by excretion? *(1)*

b) i) The diagram shows the human urinary system, with parts labelled A, B, C, D and E.

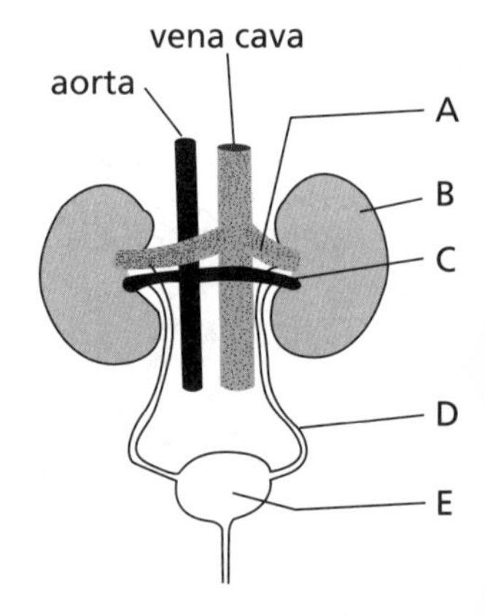

The table lists descriptions of some parts of the urinary system. Match letters from the diagram to their descriptions in the table. Letters may be used more than once. Write one letter only in each box. *(4)*

Description	Letter
1 stores urine	
2 contents do not contain urea	
3 where nephrons are found	
4 carries oxygen to the kidney	

ii) Name the tube carrying urine away from the bladder. *(1)*

c) The hormone adrenaline is produced by the adrenal glands. Draw a label line with an **X** on the diagram to show the position of an adrenal gland. *(1)*

d) Adrenaline is secreted when a person is frightened. Explain **two** ways in which adrenaline prepares the body for immediate action. *(4)*

5 The diagram shows a nephron from a kidney.

a) i) Name the parts of the nephron labelled A, B and C. *(3)*

ii) Describe the process of ultrafiltration, which occurs when the blood passes through the glomerulus. *(2)*

iii) Give **two** ways in which the glomerular filtrate differs from blood plasma. *(2)*

b) Describe what happens to the glucose in the filtrate as it passes through part B. *(3)*

c) Describe **two** functions of part C. *(2)*

(Total = 12 marks)

Applying principles

Example

1 Normal human body temperature lies within narrow limits, between 36 and 38 °C. External air temperatures can range from –50 °C to 50 °C (and further, beyond the range quoted).

To keep the body temperature within the required limits, there must be a balance between heat gained and heat lost by the body. Heat gains and losses can be represented by the diagram.

heat gain		heat loss
heat generated in the body heat gained from outside	=	evaporation of sweat conduction convection radiation

a) What term is used to describe the maintenance of the internal environment of an organism within the required limits? *(1)*

b) Suggest **one** way that the human body can generate heat and **one** way that the body can gain heat from outside. *(2)*

c) The table lists some descriptions of different situations linked to temperature control. For each situation, explain how the body temperature is kept within the required limits or how the statement is linked to temperature control mechanisms. Copy the table and write an explanation for each description. *(8)*

Description	Explanation
1 After running a race a person's face often becomes redder.	(1)
2 In hot desert areas, traditional clothing often consists of several layers of loose white clothing covering the whole body.	(2)
3 A person wearing wet clothes when walking in cold mountains on a windy day soon feels very cold.	(3)
4 On a hot and humid day, a person sweats a lot but still feels uncomfortably hot.	(4)

(Total = 11 marks)

Student 1 response Total 6/11	Marker comments and tips for success
a) *Osmoregulation* O	Osmoregulation is one example of homeostasis but is not enough to cover the wider meaning of homeostasis.
b) *You can wrap a blanket around you, and you will soon get warm.* O *To get hot from outside you can go out into the sun.* ✓	Wrapping a blanket around a person is a way of insulating them, so that their body heat is trapped inside. Body heat is generated by respiration and by other metabolic activities.
c) (1) *A runner gets very hot. The blood vessels in the skin widen* ✓ *and move up to the surface* O *so more blood reaches the skin. The face looks red.*	The first part of the answer is correct and gains 1 mark. However, the capillaries in the skin do not move. This is a common misunderstanding. The arterioles near the skin widen (vasodilation), and this allows more blood to flow through the capillaries near the skin surface.
(2) *The layers of clothes trap air* ✓ *which is a good insulator.* ✓ *So less heat reaches the body from the sun.* (✓)	A third valid point was made, indicated by the brackets, but the maximum for the question had been reached.
(3) *Clothes trap air, which is a good insulator and keeps you warm.* ✓ *Wet clothes contain water not air, so don't insulate you as well.* ✓	Student 1 gained full credit for making a valid alternative point and explaining it. 'eq' on the mark scheme shows that other valid points are allowed.

(continued)

Student 1 response Total 6/11	Marker comments and tips for success
(4) The body has ways of cooling itself, but sometimes the temperature is so high that even sweating isn't enough. ○	The student missed the implication of the word 'humid'. To cool the body the sweat has to evaporate, taking heat from the body (latent heat) to enable it to become water vapour. If the air is humid it is nearly saturated with water vapour, so evaporation is reduced and the body isn't cooled.

Student 2 response Total 10/11	Marker comments and tips for success
a) Homeostasis ✔	This is the correct term.
b) When muscles in the body contract, heat will be generated. ✔ You can get heat from outside by being close to a fire. ✔	The answer correctly describes how the body can gain heat.
c) (1) Running a race makes you very hot. Heat must be lost quickly. Vasodilation ✔ occurs and more blood flows through the capillaries near the surface of the skin. ✔ This is why the face looks redder.	Correct reference is made to vasodilation and to the increased blood flow in the capillaries.
(2) The sun glares down so you need to have white clothes to reduce the amount of heat reaching the body. ✔	1 mark for understanding that the traditional clothing will reduce the amount of heat absorbed from the sun. White-coloured clothes reflect heat – this detail, explaining how they reduce the heat reaching the body, had to be given to gain a mark.
(3) Water evaporates quickly ✔ in the wind, and this takes heat from the body. ✔	A carefully worded answer that gains full marks.
(4) Sweat cools the body when it evaporates, ✔ but if it can't evaporate, which happens when it's humid, ✔ then it stays on the skin and the person isn't cooled down.	Student 2 gives a description that shows understanding of the process involved.

Practice questions

2 Some volunteers took part in an investigation into sweating rates and body temperature when the body was dehydrated.

The volunteers had been deprived of water so that they had become dehydrated to different levels, up to 7% of their normal body water content. They were then exposed to heat and during this time their core body temperatures and their sweating rates were monitored. Temperature of the rectum (rectal temperature) was used as a measure of core body temperature.

Level of dehydration (%)	Sweating rate in g per m^2 per hour	Rectal temperature in °C
0	330	37.4
3	300	37.6
5	260	37.8
7	160	38.2

The table shows the sweating rates and rectal temperatures of the volunteers at different dehydration levels (0%, 3%, 5% and 7%).

a) Explain how sweating helps to cool the body when a person is hot. *(3)*

b) i) In this investigation, how does the sweating rate of the volunteers with 7% dehydration differ from the volunteers with 0% dehydration? *(2)*

ii) Suggest an explanation for the difference in sweating rate in the dehydrated volunteers. *(2)*

c) What evidence is there in the data provided that the difference in rate of sweating may have affected body temperature? *(2)*

d) How would you expect the kidneys of the volunteers to respond to dehydration? *(2)*

(Total = 11 marks)

3 Animals living in deserts need to conserve water. The kangaroo rat is a small mammal that lives in deserts in North America. The rat eats seeds and other dry plant material and never drinks.

A study was made of water balance in a kangaroo rat. The table summarises the water gains and losses of a kangaroo rat during a period of 4 weeks. During this time, the kangaroo rat consumed 100 g of barley grains for food.

Water gains in cm^3		Water losses in cm^3	
Oxidation water	54.0	Urine	13.5
Absorbed water (from the barley grains)	6.0	Feces	2.6
		Evaporation	43.6
Total	60.0	Total	60.0

a) Water is formed from the oxidation of different food molecules, including carbohydrates, lipids and proteins. Write down a balanced chemical equation to summarise how water is produced from the oxidation of glucose during respiration. *(3)*

b) The table shows that some water is lost from the kangaroo rat in the urine.

i) Calculate the percentage of water lost in the urine of the kangaroo rat. Show your working. *(2)*

ii) Where in the kidney is water reabsorbed from the kidney filtrate back into the blood? *(1)*

iii) The kangaroo rat produces very concentrated urine. Measurements show that the concentration of dissolved substances in the urine of a kangaroo rat is about 3840 arbitrary units whereas the equivalent figure for the urine of a human is 790 arbitrary units. Suggest how the kidney helps the kangaroo rat survive in the dry conditions in a desert. *(2)*

c) The feces of a kangaroo rat contained 2.6 g of water per 100 g of barley food consumed. The feces of a similar rat (which does not live in the desert) contained 13.6 g of water per 100 g of barley food consumed

i) Where is water reabsorbed from food material as it passes through the gut in the process of digestion? *(1)*

ii) Use the evidence provided to suggest how the feces of the kangaroo rat help it to survive in the dry conditions in a desert. *(2)*

d) In the table, the highest figure for water loss is for evaporation. Most of this is in exhaled air from the lungs. Explain why exhaled air contains water vapour and why, as in many mammals, it is important that there is some water vapour in the lungs. *(2)*

(Total = 13 marks)

4 Some people are unable to control their blood glucose level. The condition is known as diabetes and may occur when a person does not produce enough insulin.

A person is sometimes given a glucose tolerance test to help decide whether treatment may be appropriate. The person fasts for 8 to 12 hours, then the blood glucose level is tested. The person then drinks a large quantity of dissolved glucose and the blood glucose is measured at hourly intervals for several hours.

The graph shows the blood glucose levels of one person with diabetes and one person without diabetes during the 5 hours after a glucose drink.

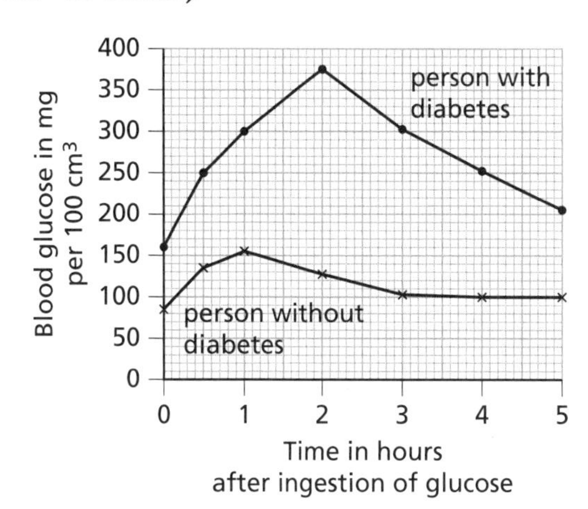

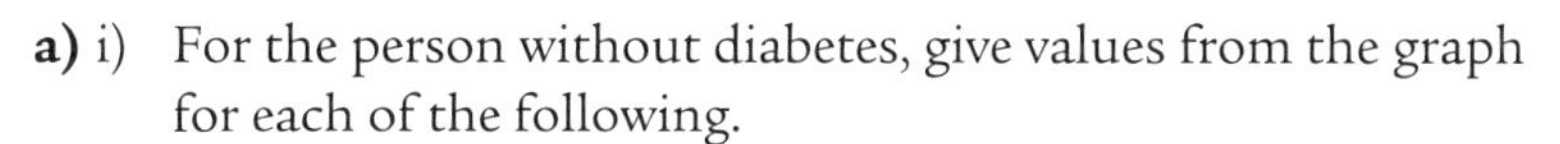

a) i) For the person without diabetes, give values from the graph for each of the following.

1 the normal blood glucose level (at the time the glucose drink is given)
2 the maximum blood glucose and when this occurs
3 the time taken for the glucose level to return to the normal level. *(3)*

ii) Describe how the results for blood glucose level of the person with diabetes differ from the results of the person without diabetes. *(3)*

b) Foods containing carbohydrates may be digested at different rates. If a person has diabetes, suggest why it may be an advantage to eat foods containing carbohydrates (such as starch) that are digested at a slower rate. *(2)*

(Total = 8 marks)

Extended writing

Example

1 A child touches a hot cooking pan but he pulls his fingers back quickly before he burns them. Describe the reflex arc that leads to the rapid movement of his fingers. *(6)*

Student 1 response

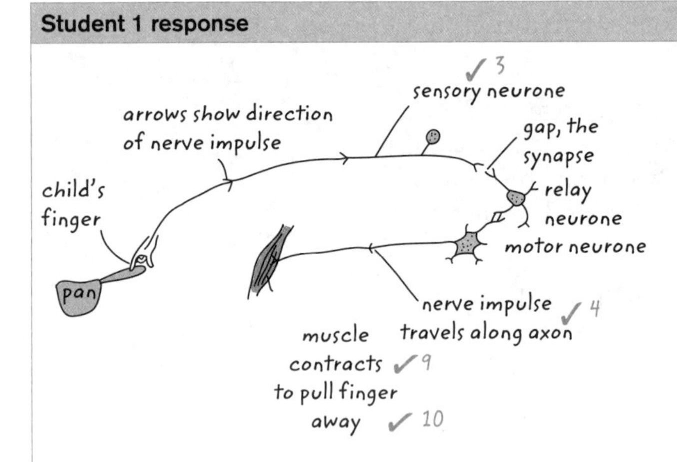

The drawing shows the pathway of the nerve impulse in a reflex arc. It travels across gaps between neurones.

Student 2 response

Plan

Receptor → message/impulse → sensory/motor? neurone → spinal cord neurone → sensory/motor? neurone → effector/muscle

Nerve fibres? spinal cord or CNS?

The receptors in the fingers feel the pain and send nerve impulses along a sensory neurone. From there it travels to a neurone in the spinal cord. The message crosses a tiny gap between the neurones, called a synapse. The impulse crosses to another neurone called the motor neurone. This carries it to the effector muscle.

Mark scheme

The mark scheme shows how marks are awarded.

(1) (pain / heat / stimulus) generates electrical / nerve impulses / eq
(2) in receptor
(3) (impulse) along sensory neurone
(4) (impulse) along axon / nerve fibre*
(5) (impulse) across synapse*
(6) (impulse) to relay / intermediate neurone
(7) in spinal cord / CNS / eq
(8) (impulse) to motor neurone
(9) (impulse) to effector / muscle
(10) (muscle) contracts (to move fingers)

**Points marked with an asterisk may be mentioned in different parts of the sequence but may only be credited once.*

Total: 6

Student 1 response Total 5/6	Marker comments and tips for success
The drawing ...	Some students find that a drawing helps them to remember the sequence of events. Draw it quickly (you only have about 3 minutes for planning) and *annotate* it to explain what happens. You will then have about 3 minutes to *describe what happens*.
... shows the pathway of the nerve impulse in a reflex arc.	Mark (1) not given. This mark is for linking the stimulus (the heat or pain) to the generation of the nerve impulse.

(continued)

Student 1 response Total 5/6	Marker comments and tips for success
Marks awarded on the diagram: *(3) ✔ (impulse) along sensory neurone* *(4) ✔ (impulse) along axon/nerve fibre** *(9) ✔ (impulse) to effector/muscle* *(10) ✔ (muscle) contracts (to move fingers)*	The labelled arrow showing the direction of the nerve impulse, together with the labelled sensory neurone, gains mark (3). Marks (4) and (10) were given for the annotations on the diagram. Mark (9) was given for the arrow showing the nerve impulse travelling along the axon towards the labelled muscle.
Marks not awarded on the diagram: *(5) (impulse) across synapse O* *(6) (impulse) to relay/intermediate neurone O* *(8) (impulse) to motor neurone O*	The synapse is labelled correctly, with a label line joining it to the 'gap'. However, mark (5) was not awarded because the diagram was not annotated to explain that the nerve impulse travels across the gap. The diagram must have appropriate annotations attached (with label lines) to gain the marks. Marks (6) and (8) were not awarded because without label lines, no credit can be given for 'relay neurone' and 'motor neurone'.
It travels across gaps ✔ between neurones	Mark (5) can be given now because the student explains that the impulse crosses the 'gaps', and the gap is identified on the diagram as the synapse.

Student 2 response Total 6/6	Marker comments and tips for success
Plan Receptor → message/impulse → sensory/motor? neurone → spinal cord neurone → sensory/motor? neurone → effector/muscle Nerve fibres? spinal cord or CNS?	It is a good idea to take a few minutes, before you write your answer, to plan what you should include. A flow diagram is a useful way to do this. You can cross the plan out when you have finished.
The receptors ✔ in the fingers feel the pain and send nerve impulses ... ✔	Mark (2) for receptor and mark (1) for pain causing the nerve impulses.
... along a sensory neurone. ✔	Mark (3) awarded.
From there it travels to a neurone in the spinal cord. ✔	Mark (7) awarded.
The message crosses a tiny gap between the neurones, called a synapse. ✔	Mark (5) awarded. The student refers to the impulse as a 'message'. It is better to avoid using imprecise words. Learn and use the correct terms.
The impulse crosses to another neurone called the motor neurone. ✔	Mark (8) awarded.
This carries it to the effector (✔) muscle (✔).	Two more marks could be awarded if the maximum for the question had not been reached.

Extended writing questions – general advice

When answering this type of question it is preferable to make sure that you give a complete written description rather than relying entirely on a diagram. You can provide explanations in a written account that are more difficult to convey on a diagram. On the other hand, a diagram can help you to remember the key points, and a clear diagram with appropriate annotations can gain high marks, as here.

For further advice on the extended writing questions, see pages 72 and 85.

Practice questions

2 An athlete runs a 2000 m race. Describe how heat is produced and lost to keep his body temperature constant during the race. *(6)*

3 Describe the process of ultrafiltration in the kidney nephron. *(6)*

4 Dancers sweat heavily while practising. Describe how ADH helps to keep the water content of their blood at normal levels during a rehearsal. *(6)*

5 Reproduction and inheritance

Using and interpreting data

Example

1 White tigers are rare in the wild, but carefully recorded breeding programmes in zoos have led to an increase in their number.

In one zoo, a white tiger cub was born to two tigers with orange fur. In tigers, the allele for orange fur (**F**) is dominant to the allele for white fur (**f**). Tigers with white fur are homozygous for the recessive allele.

a) Explain what is meant by the term **allele**. *(2)*

b) For the tigers described above, use a genetic diagram to show:
- the genotype of each parent
- the gametes they produced
- the possible genotypes of all the offspring
- the possible phenotypes of all the offspring. *(4)*

c) State the probability that the next tiger cub born to these parents would also be white. *(1)*

d) Suggest reasons why white tigers are rarely found in the wild. *(2)*

(Total = 9 marks)

Student 1 response Total 5/9	Marker comments and tips for success
a) *Alleles are different versions of a gene.* ✔ *They are made of DNA and found on the locus of a chromosome.*	Only part of the definition has been given. It is not made clear that all the alleles of a gene are found at the same locus (position) on a chromosome. Make sure you know the standard definitions, as the concepts can be difficult to explain. It is helpful to give an example (see student 2).
b) *Parents:* Ff × Ff ✔ parent genotypes no gametes O *Genotypes of offspring:* FF Ff FF ff dark dark dark white offspring genotypes O *phenotypes* ✔ phenotypes	One mark for working out the parent genotypes (**Ff**). A white cub is homozygous recessive, so it must be genotype **ff**. It must have received one **f** allele from each parent. The parents are orange, so must both have the dominant **F** allele as well. The student did not put the expected 'gamete' line in the diagram – no mark. There was a mistake in doing the crossing, so the offspring genotypes were incorrect – no mark. A mark for phenotype was allowed because the student indicated the phenotype shown by each of the three possible genotypes, even though the ratio of genotypes was incorrect. 'Dark' was accepted for 'orange fur'. Practise setting out cross diagrams correctly so you don't forget anything. Note: you should write 'phenotypes' on the left, not underneath.
c) *25%* ✔	From the cross diagram, one of the four possible outcomes of fertilisation would give a white cub, a probability of 1 in 4 or 25%. Even though the student made a mistake in b), the probability from his cross happens to be the same as for the correct cross.
d) *White tigers will be seen more easily* ✔ *by predators.*	A little more explanation is needed for a second mark, such as a link to humans killing or capturing white tigers.

Student 2 response Total 7/9	Marker comments and tips for success
a) Alleles are alternative forms of a gene ✔ and are found at the same position on a chromosome. ✔ For example, T and t are alternative forms of the gene for height in pea plants.	Full marks. If you learn the definitions it helps you to give the correct answer. The example is also worth a mark (see mark scheme) but the maximum for the question has been reached.
b) parents O female gametes: F f ✓gametes male gametes F: FF, Ff male gametes f: Ff, ff white ✓offspring genotypes phenotypes: 3 orange: 1 white phenotypes (not linked to genotypes) O	The student used a Punnett square to work out the possible offspring genotypes. This is recommended for more complicated crosses as it prevents the kind of crossing error made by student 1. • A common error is to forget to put in the parents (as here) or to forget to label the gametes or the possible genotypes of the offspring. • The student should have listed the possible offspring genotypes underneath the diagram. The phenotypes of the possible offspring can then be written in below the genotypes. • Student 2 has not indicated the phenotypes (fur colours) for each of the three genotypes. She has only given the phenotype (white) for **ff**.
c) 1 in 4 ✔	Fusion of gametes at fertilisation occurs randomly, and only one of the four possible outcomes gives a cub with genotype **ff**. The probability that the next cub will be white is therefore 1 in 4. In part b), Student 2 recorded the ratio of possible phenotypes as 1 white : 3 orange. This ratio is not a probability, but you can use the ratio to work out that the probability is 1 in 4.
d) Recessive alleles only show in the homozygous recessive ✔ white tiger. ✔ This is only produced from a mating between two tigers who are heterozygous. There are so few tigers that might meet and mate that the chance of this happening is very small.	The marks are given for recognising that the allele for white fur is recessive, so only shows in the phenotype if there is no dominant allele present ('homozygous recessive white tiger').

Practice questions

2 Huntington's disease in humans is an inherited disorder that affects the adult nervous system. It is caused by a dominant allele, **H**. A person without the disease is homozygous for the recessive allele, **h**.

a) Show how the disease may be passed on even if just one parent is heterozygous for Huntington's disease and the other parent is normal.

Use a genetic diagram to show:
- the genotype of each parent
- the gametes they might produce
- the possible genotypes of the children
- the possible phenotypes of the children. *(4)*

b) State the probability of a child of these parents inheriting the condition. *(1)*

(Total = 5 marks)

3 The colour of the hairs on the skin of cattle is inherited.

The colour of the hairs is controlled by a gene with two alleles. The alleles are codominant. The allele **R** codes for red hairs and the allele **W** codes for white hairs. Cattle with both alleles in their genotype (**RW**) have a mixture of red and white hairs, and this is called roan.

a) Explain what is meant by **codominance**. *(2)*

b) A roan cow was mated with a roan bull. Use a genetic diagram to show:
- the genotype of each parent
- the gametes they produced
- the possible genotypes of all the offspring
- the possible phenotypes of all the offspring. *(4)*

c) State the probability that one of the offspring was roan. *(1)*

d) i) Explain what is meant by the term **heterozygous**. *(2)*

ii) Draw a circle around **one** heterozygous individual shown in your genetic diagram. *(1)*

(Total = 10 marks)

4 Many studies of genetic crosses are cases in which the phenotype is determined by a pair of alleles and one allele is dominant over the other allele.

a) What is meant by the term **dominant allele**? *(1)*

In one study, scientists crossed pea plants homozygous for round seeds with pea plants that were homozygous for wrinkled seeds. All the offspring had round seeds.

b) Use a genetic diagram to show the parent genotypes, the gametes formed and the genotypes of the offspring. *(3)*

c) The offspring plants were allowed to self-pollinate and 500 of the seeds they produced were grown into mature plants. Of these, 368 plants had round seeds and 132 plants had wrinkled seeds.

i) This result is close to the 3:1 phenotypic ratio the scientists expected to see. Suggest reasons why the ratio was not exactly 3:1. *(2)*

ii) Give the genotypes of the offspring obtained from the self-pollinated plants. *(1)*

(Total = 7 marks)

5 Fruit flies are often used to study patterns of inheritance. In an investigation, the inheritance of their eye colour was studied. The allele for red eyes (**R**) is dominant to the allele for white eyes (**r**).

a) i) What is meant by the term **genotype**? *(1)*

ii) What are the **two** possible genotypes for a fly with red eyes? *(1)*

b) A heterozygous red-eyed fly was mated with a white-eyed fly. Draw a genetic diagram to show:

- the parent genotypes
- the gametes they produced
- the genotypes of the possible offspring
- the phenotypes of the possible offspring. *(4)*

c) Give the genotype and phenotype of the offspring produced by mating a homozygous red-eyed fly with a white-eyed fly. *(2)*

d) In a sample of 50 offspring from the mating of a red-eyed fly with a white-eyed fly, scientists found 21 flies with white eyes. From this result, what was the genotype of the red-eyed parent fly? *(1)*

(Total = 9 marks)

Understanding structure, function and processes

Example

1 The diagrams show the chromosomes present in four cells.

A

B

C

D

a) Which structure in a cell contains the chromosomes? *(1)*

b) i) From the diagram, give the letter of one cell that is diploid and give a reason for your answer. *(2)*

ii) Which cell could have divided by meiosis to produce cell D? *(1)*

iii) Cell C divides once by mitosis.

1 How many daughter cells will there be?

2 How many chromosomes will there be in each daughter cell? *(2)*

c) Chromosomes carry the genetic code in the form of DNA. Describe the structure of DNA. *(4)*

(Total = 10 marks)

Student 1 response Total 5/10	Marker comments and tips for success
a) *nucleus* ✔	Correct.
b) i) *C* ✔ *A diploid cell has two sets of chromosomes.* ✔	The student counted the number of chromosomes in each cell and also looked at their shapes. He saw that C had two sets of four chromosomes.
ii) *A* O	Student 1 has probably mixed up mitosis and meiosis. Cell division by meiosis halves the number of chromosomes, so cell B, with six chromosomes (three pairs) is the only one that could have produced D, with three chromosomes.
iii) *daughter cells = 4* O *chromosomes in each = 4* O	Student 1 has again confused mitosis with meiosis. If cell C divided by meiosis there would be four daughter cells each with four chromosomes. However, if a cell divides by mitosis two daughter cells are produced, each with the same number of chromosomes as the parent.
c) *DNA is a very long molecule* ✔ *that coils up to make a chromosome. The strands are made up of bases paired together, like adenine and thymine.* ✔ *The sequence of the bases is the code the cell uses to make its enzymes.*	'Coils up' is not equivalent to 'double helix'. Student 1 needed to put in more details about DNA structure to gain more marks. He could have mentioned the two strands in the DNA molecule, and listed all four bases, to get full marks.

Student 2 response Total 9/10	Marker comments and tips for success
a) nucleus ✔	Correct.
b) i) B ✔ It has 3 pairs of similar chromosomes. ✔	One mark for stating that cell B was diploid and a second mark for the reason.
ii) B ✔	Cell D has only three chromosomes. The cell that divided by meiosis to produce D must be diploid, with two sets of three chromosomes (cell B).
iii) Two cells ✔, each with 8 chromosomes. ✔	Full marks.
c) A DNA molecule is made up of two strands ✔ with four bases joined together in a particular order, ✔ which is the genetic code. Although there are only four bases, for example A, B O and C, these can make up the thousands of different genes. The two strands are coiled together in a double helix. ✔	For a further mark, student 2 needed to name (or give the symbols for) all four of the bases. 'B' is not a symbol for a DNA base. Alternatively, she could have said that A pairs with T or G pairs with C.

Practice questions

2 The diagram shows the structure of a flower.

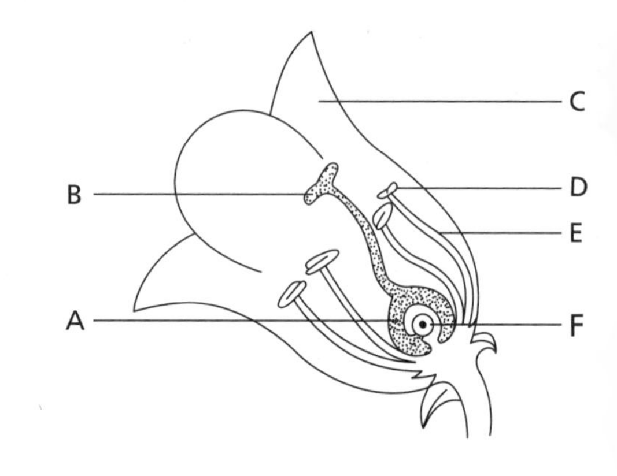

a) Name parts **B** and **C**. *(2)*

b) The table lists some events that occur during reproduction. Complete the table using letters from the diagram to show where each event occurs. Letters may be used more than once. Write **one** letter only in each box. *(4)*

Event	Letter
1 male gametes are produced	
2 a pollen tube begins to grow	
3 fertilisation takes place	
4 the fruit may develop	

c) Give the letters of **two** structures where cell division by meiosis takes place. *(2)*

d) i) Explain what is meant by the term **pollination**. *(2)*

ii) Describe **three** ways a flower may be adapted for pollination by insects. *(3)*

e) Some plants can reproduce both sexually, by producing seeds, and asexually, by producing runners.

i) Describe **two** ways in which asexual reproduction differs from sexual reproduction. *(2)*

ii) Explain why sexual reproduction can be an advantage to the plant. *(2)*

(Total = 17 marks)

3 The diagram shows the male reproductive organs.

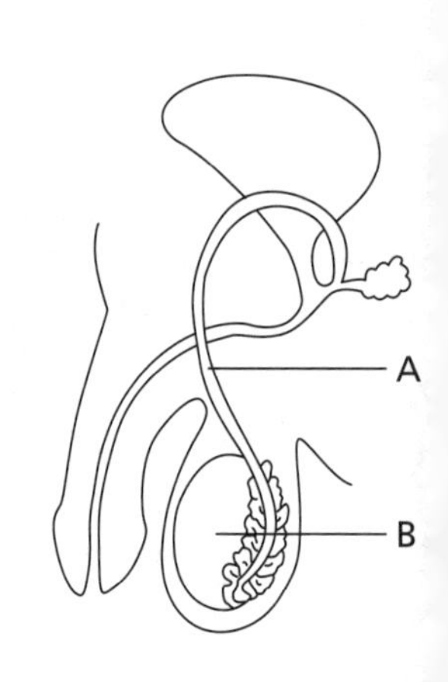

a) Name parts **A** and **B**. *(2)*

b) Name the tube that carries two different fluids at certain times. *(1)*

c) Draw a label line with an **M** on the diagram to show an organ where meiosis takes place. *(1)*

d) i) Name the organ that secretes testosterone. *(1)*

ii) During puberty, testosterone secretion leads to the growth of hair on the body. Describe a secondary sexual characteristic, other than hair growth, that also develops during puberty in a male. *(1)*

e) i) Explain what is meant by **fertilisation**. *(2)*

ii) Explain how the **X** and **Y** chromosomes, carried by the gametes of the parents, determine the sex of a child. *(3)*

iii) What is the probability that a child will be a boy? *(1)*

(Total = 12 marks)

4 A gardener shows some students how to grow plants successfully from seed. He explains that the soil must be moist, but not so wet that there are no air spaces left in the soil.

a) i) Explain why a seed needs water to germinate. *(2)*

ii) Explain why a seed needs air to germinate. *(2)*

b) The students prepared some pots of sunflower seeds for germination. They kept one group of pots at 20 °C and another group at 10 °C.

Explain why the seeds that were kept at 20 °C germinated before the seeds kept at 10 °C. *(2)*

c) Name the type of cell division taking place in growing seedlings. *(1)*

(Total = 7 marks)

5 The diagram shows the female reproductive organs.

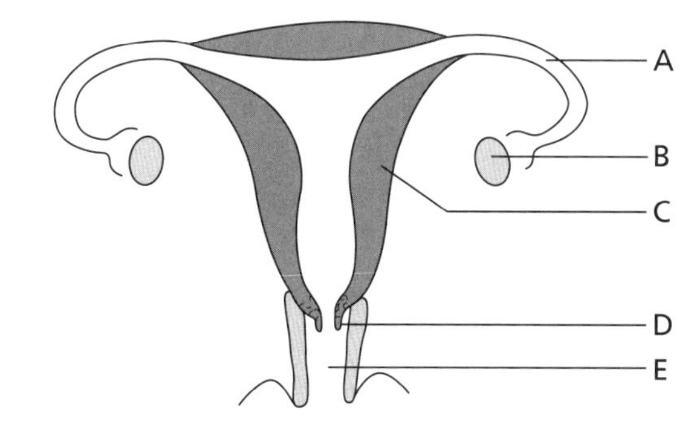

a) Name parts **A** and **E**. *(2)*

b) The table lists some events that occur in the female reproductive system. Complete the table using letters from the diagram to show where each event occurs. Letters may be used more than once. Write **one** letter only in each box. *(4)*

Event	Letter
1 meiosis takes place	
2 fertilisation takes place	
3 an egg cell is produced	
4 a placenta develops	

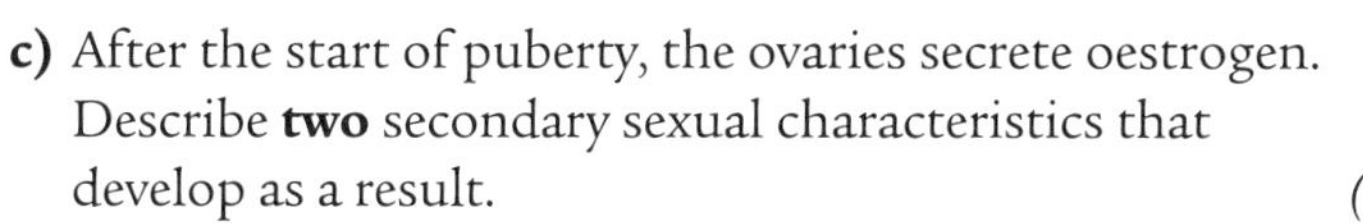

c) After the start of puberty, the ovaries secrete oestrogen. Describe **two** secondary sexual characteristics that develop as a result. *(2)*

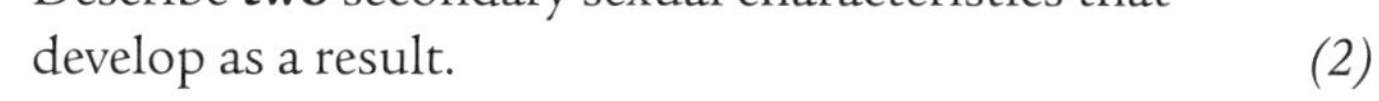

d) i) Where is progesterone secreted from? *(1)*

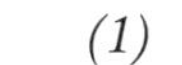

ii) Describe **one** effect of progesterone. *(1)*

e) The diagram shows changes in the levels of oestrogen and progesterone for the first 14 days of a 28-day menstrual cycle.

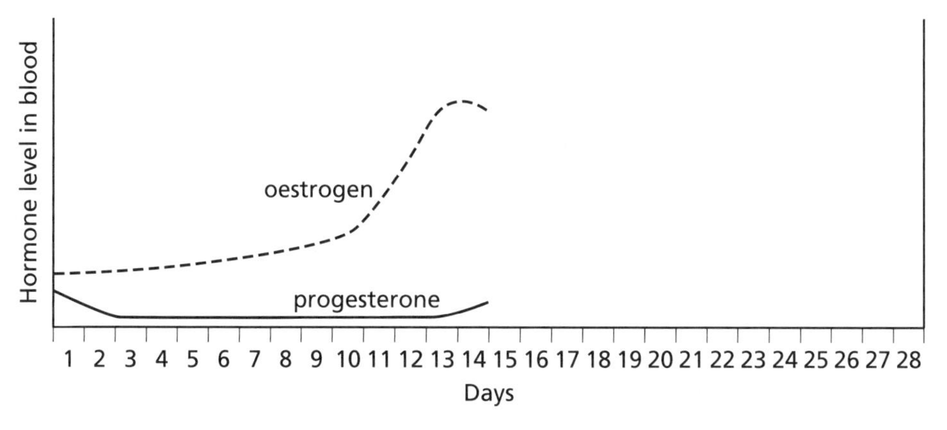

i) Continue the graph lines for oestrogen and progesterone to show the levels that you would expect from day 14 to day 28, if the woman does not become pregnant. *(2)*

ii) The uterus lining becomes thicker during the menstrual cycle. Explain why the thicker lining is important if a fertilised egg cell is to develop into a fetus. *(2)*

(Total = 14 marks)

Applying principles

Example

1 Cystic fibrosis is a disorder that causes the production of very sticky mucus in the lungs.

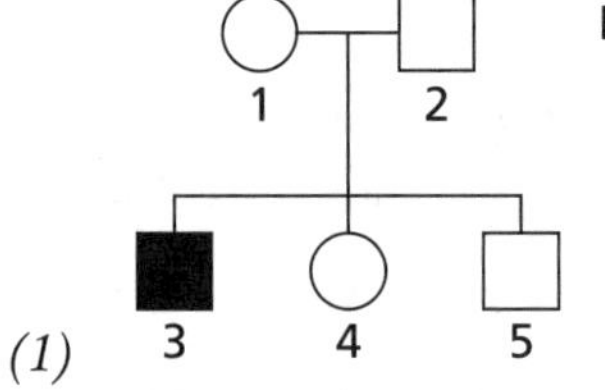

a) The family tree shows the pattern of inheritance of cystic fibrosis in one family. How many females have cystic fibrosis? *(1)*

b) i) Explain what is meant by the term **recessive**. *(2)*

ii) Explain how you can tell that cystic fibrosis is a recessive characteristic. *(2)*

c) i) Identify **one** person who is definitely homozygous. *(1)*

ii) Identify **one** person who is definitely heterozygous. *(1)*

d) i) What are the genotypes of parent 1 and parent 2? Use **F** to represent the normal allele and **f** to represent the allele for cystic fibrosis. *(2)*

ii) What is the probability that the next child of parents 1 and 2 will have cystic fibrosis? *(1)*

(Total = 10 marks)

Student 1 response Total 3/10	Marker comments and tips for success
a) *Two* O	You must look at a family tree question very carefully. Underline the key facts, such as the meaning of the symbols. This would have made it clear that there were no females with cystic fibrosis.
b) i) *A gene* O *is recessive if it doesn't show when the dominant gene is present,* ✔ *e.g. two parents with brown eyes have a child with blue eyes. So the parents had the blue eye gene but it was hidden.*	Only an allele of a gene can be recessive. Misuse of 'gene' and 'allele' accounts for many lost marks – if unsure, use 'allele'. The student should have said '... (recessive) doesn't show in the phenotype ...' but by quoting blue / brown eyes – an example of phenotype – he just got the mark. Genetics questions often ask for a definition. These can be difficult to explain, so make sure you know them.
ii) *Because it only shows in the children,* O *not the parents.* ✔	This answer just missed a second mark. The student has used evidence from the family tree, but as only one of the three children showed cystic fibrosis, use of the plural 'children' indicates lack of understanding. Be precise when quoting evidence and leave time to check your answers.
c) i) *Person 1, 3* O	Students often mix up homozygous and heterozygous. Person 1 is heterozygous and person 3 is homozygous, with two similar recessive alleles. Make sure you know which is which, and learn the definitions. If asked for one answer, only put one answer down. Right answer + wrong answer = 0.
ii) *Person 4* O	From b) ii), the student should realise that parents 1 and 2 are heterozygous. The genotype of person 4, showing the dominant characteristic, could be homozygous or heterozygous. To answer these questions confidently, make sure you are familiar with the patterns of inheritance for the four typical dominant / recessive crosses and codominant crosses.
d) i) *Parent 1, Ff* ✔ *and parent 2, FF* O	From b) ii), the student should deduce that the genotype of both parents, 1 and 2, is **Ff**.
ii) *Ff X FF* *possible gametes F f F F* *possible offspring FF FF Ff Ff* *ratio 1:1, normal: cystic fibrosis* O	The student is right to work out the probability by drawing a cross diagram, although there are no marks for the diagram itself. Unfortunately, although the crossing method is correct, the genotypes used were wrong. No credit can be given for transfer error across different question parts.

Student 2 response Total 9/10	Marker comments and tips for success
a) *No females have cystic fibrosis* ✔	Correct.
b) i) *A recessive allele* ✔ *only shows in the phenotype if the other allele is the same.* ✔ *E.g. a person will only have blue eyes if they are genotype bb.*	A good answer. The student has quoted a recognised definition. Although it is advisable to give an example, full marks were gained without one.
ii) *The offspring, child 3, has cystic fibrosis* ✔ *even though neither parent had it.* ✔ *The parents were both normal.*	Full marks.
c) i) *Person 3* ✔	A person showing the recessive characteristic must be homozygous, carrying two similar recessive alleles.
ii) *Parent 1* ✔	A person showing the dominant characteristic (normal) could be homozygous or heterozygous. The only individuals whose genotype is certainly heterozygous, because they had a child with cystic fibrosis (homozygous recessive) are the parents, individuals 1 and 2.
d) i) *Both parents are Ff.* ✔ ✔	Full marks.
ii) *Ff × Ff* (Punnett square: columns F, f; row F: FF, Ff; row f: Ff, ff) *1:3 ratio* O	A Punnett square is less likely to lead to error than a cross diagram. (A student who has practised crosses will know the outcomes without a diagram.) No mark because the student did not identify the phenotypes that the ratio referred to, but in any case this is not the same as the probability. 0.25, 25%, ¼ or 1 in 4 are all acceptable ways of quoting the probability in this example.

	F	f
F	FF	Ff
f	Ff	ff

Practice questions

2 Hair length in cats is controlled by a pair of alleles, and one of the alleles is dominant over the other allele.

A cat breeder keeps genetic records for her cats. The diagram shows part of a family tree showing the distribution of hair length in her cats.

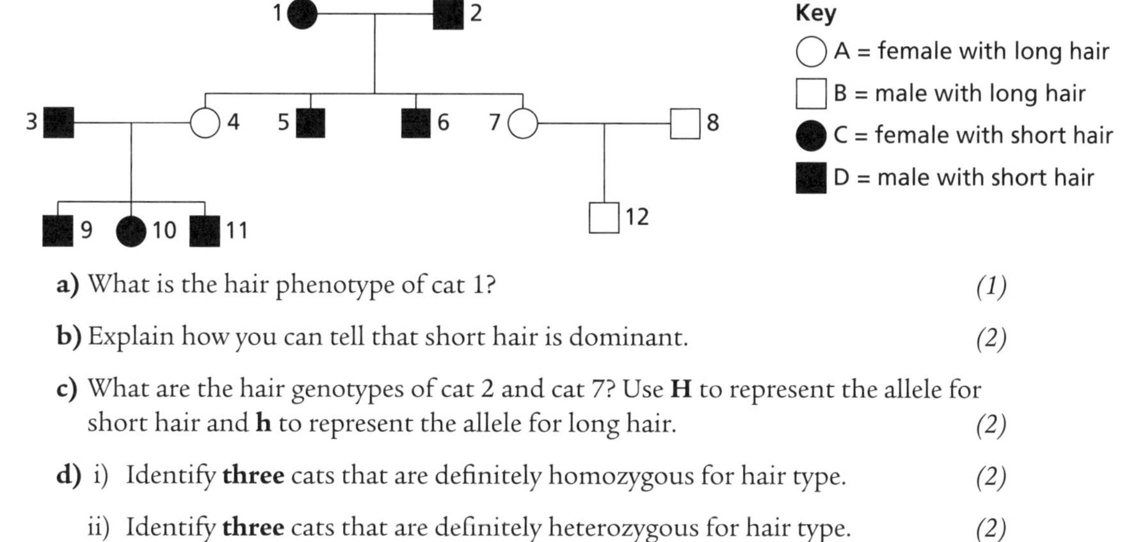

a) What is the hair phenotype of cat 1? *(1)*

b) Explain how you can tell that short hair is dominant. *(2)*

c) What are the hair genotypes of cat 2 and cat 7? Use **H** to represent the allele for short hair and **h** to represent the allele for long hair. *(2)*

d) i) Identify **three** cats that are definitely homozygous for hair type. *(2)*

ii) Identify **three** cats that are definitely heterozygous for hair type. *(2)*

(Total = 9 marks)

3 Scientists wanted to develop crop plants resistant to weedkillers. This would allow them to use weedkillers to control weeds but not damage crop plants. The diagram on the next page shows one way of doing this.

a) Explain the effects that X-rays might have on the multiplying cells (step 2). *(2)*

b) Cells **A**, **B**, **C** and **D** came from the same plant and had the same alleles. Suggest why, after treatment with X-rays, plant cell **C** is able to grow in the dish containing weedkiller (step 4) whereas cells **A**, **B** and **D** do not. *(2)*

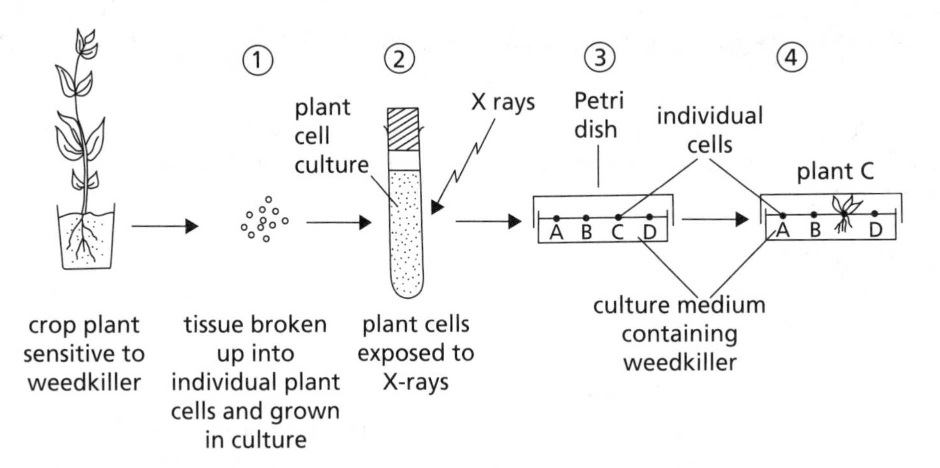

c) The scientists were able to grow large numbers of resistant plants from plant **C** by taking cuttings. Suggest why they chose to take cuttings rather than allowing plant **C** to produce seeds. *(2)*

(Total = 6 marks)

4 A group of students investigated the change in mass of seeds during and after germination.

They sowed sweet pea seeds in identical pots of soil, putting 15 seeds in each pot. The pots were kept in warm, light conditions and watered regularly. At intervals the students removed ten seedlings. They were placed in an oven at 100 °C until all water had evaporated from the cells. The students recorded the dry mass of the 10 seedlings.

The results are shown in the graph.

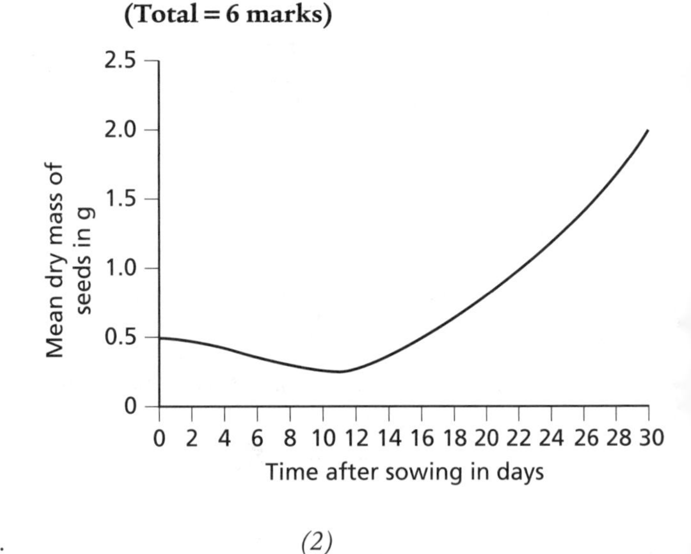

a) Explain the changes in the dry mass over the 30 days shown in the graph. *(3)*

b) Explain the shape of the graph from day 0 to day 10. *(2)*

c) i) From the graph, on which day did the seedlings begin to carry out photosynthesis? *(1)*

ii) Explain your answer. *(2)*

(Total = 8 marks)

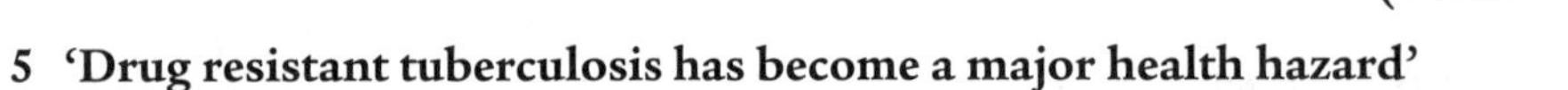

5 'Drug resistant tuberculosis has become a major health hazard'

Headline taken from a report by, England's chief medical officer in 2013.

Tuberculosis (TB) is a disease in humans caused by bacteria living in the lungs. Antibiotic drugs such as isoniazid affect the metabolism of the bacteria, causing them to die. Occasionally, some TB bacteria mutate and become resistant to one or more drugs and this has led to an increase in the number of human deaths caused by the disease.

a) What is the meaning of the term **mutation**? *(2)*

b) A rare mutation occurs that enables a TB bacterium to survive treatment with an antibiotic. Explain how this may lead to the mutation becoming widespread in the bacterial population. *(4)*

c) A report on a health service website states 'Many TB patients fail to complete their antibiotic treatment, a factor which has caused the rise in drug-resistant forms'.

Suggest why completing the course of antibiotics reduces the likelihood of drug-resistant forms multiplying. *(2)*

(Total = 8 marks)

Extended writing

Example

1 Describe how transfer of pollen grains onto the stigma of a flower can lead to fertilisation and fruit formation. *(6)*

Student 1 response
The pollen lands on the stigma and starts to grow a pollen tube. It grows down to the ovary, where the seeds are. The male gamete goes down the pollen tube to the seed and fertilises it. The seeds can then grow into a juicy fruit. Animals like to eat it and take it away. The new plants germinate and grow somewhere far away.
Student 2 response
When a pollen grain germinates on the stigma, the pollen tube starts to grow. It produces enzymes to digest its way through the style. Inside the ovary, the male nucleus fuses with the female nucleus in the ovule. The ovule can grow into a seed and the ovary, which contains the seeds, grows into a fruit.
Mark scheme
The mark scheme shows how marks are awarded. (1) (pollen) tube grows / pollen grain germinates (2) (grows down) style (3) digestion / enzymes (involved) (4) ovary (appropriate ref linked to pollen tube growth / ovules) (5) (pollen tube / male gamete) enters ovule / eq (6) through micropyle (7) (male) nucleus / (pollen grain) nucleus / male gamete (8) fertilisation / fuse / join + female gamete / nucleus / ovum / egg or ref to zygote formation (9) ovule becomes seed (10) ovule wall becomes seed coat / testa (11) ovary becomes fruit / correct reference to other parts of the flower forming part of the fruit Total: 6

Student 1 response Total 3/6	Marker comments and tips for success
The pollen lands on the stigma and starts to grow a pollen tube. ✓	Mark (1) awarded.
It grows down to the ovary, ✓ where the seeds are.	Mark (4) awarded.
The male gamete goes down the pollen tube to the seed O and fertilises ✓ it.	The correct description of the male gamete travelling down the pollen tube, together with the idea that this is essential for fertilisation to occur, was just enough for mark (7). However, the mark was nearly lost because the student implied that the male gamete fertilised the seed. The seed develops from the ovule after fertilisation.
The seeds can then grow into a juicy fruit. O	The seeds are part of the fruit, not the fruit itself.
Animals like to eat it and take it away. The new plants germinate and grow somewhere far away. O	Student 1 wasted time by writing about seed dispersal. The question asked only for fruit formation.

Student 2 response Total 6/6	Marker comments and tips for success
When a pollen grain germinates ✔ on the stigma, the pollen tube starts to grow.	Mark (1) awarded.
It produces enzymes ✔ to digest its way ...	Mark (3) awarded.
... through the style. ✔	Mark (2) is awarded for the route of the pollen tube, not just for the word 'style'.
Inside the ovary ... ✔	Mark (4) is not awarded for the word 'ovary' on its own, but for linking the ovary with the ovule and fertilisation. Aim to put the role of the various parts into a logical order, as very often the marks are awarded only if the sequence of events is correct.
... the male nucleus ... ✔	Mark (7) awarded for describing the part played by the male nucleus.
... fuses with the female nucleus ... ✔	Mark (8) awarded.
... in the ovule. (✔)	Mark (5) could be awarded (but maximum for the question, 6 marks, already reached).
The ovule can grow into a seed ... (✔)	Mark (9) could be awarded (but maximum for the question, 6 marks, already reached).
... and the ovary, which contains the seeds, grows into a fruit. (✔)	Mark (11) could be awarded (but maximum for the question, 6 marks, already reached).

Extended writing questions – general advice

- Before starting to write, pick out the key words (*fertilisation* and *fruit formation*), mark them in some way, and think carefully about what is being asked.
- This is the time to make a brief list of events for each process. It will help you to start the sequence at the right place (e.g. pollination is not wanted here) and to stop at the right place (seed dispersal is not asked for).
- If you can't remember what happens, but can remember the diagram of a pollen tube growing, a quick drawing might help to stimulate your memory. By doing this, student 1 might have remembered the 'style' and the 'ovule'. Putting them into the sequence would have gained two more marks.
- The description of events in student 2's answer is given in the correct sequence, and links the parts of the flower to their role in fertilisation. When you answer similar questions it is important to make a brief plan, so you can check that nothing is missing from the sequence before you start writing.
- For further general advice on answering the extended writing questions see pages 72 and 85.

Practice questions

2 Describe how pollination and fertilisation take place in a wind-pollinated flower. *(6)*

3 Describe **two** methods of asexual reproduction in flowering plants and explain the advantages to the plant of asexual reproduction by natural means. *(6)*

4 Describe the role of hormones in the control of the menstrual cycle. *(6)*

5 Describe the theory of natural selection and show how it may lead to evolution. *(6)*

6 Ecology and the environment

Using and interpreting data

Example

1 Some students carried out an experiment in class to help them understand the causes and effects of acid rain.

They grew wheat seedlings in small containers, as shown in the diagram. They watered the seedlings in three different ways. The first group of seedlings was watered with distilled water. The second and third groups were watered with solutions to which some dilute sulfuric acid had been added. This was adjusted to give solutions of different pH (5.5 and 4.5).

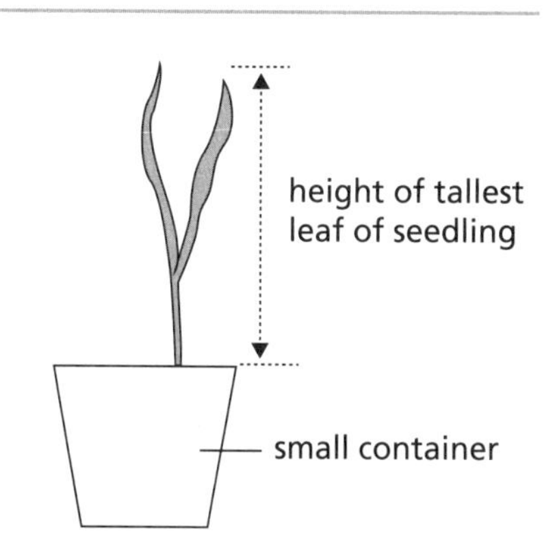

After 2 weeks they measured the heights of the seedlings in all the containers. Their results are shown in the table.

Seedling pot	Height of seedling in cm		
	pH 7.0	pH 5.5	pH 4.5
A	14	5	4
B	11	8	2
C	14	7	5
D	13	5	3
E	11	8	4
F	12	9	2
G	15	5	4
H	14	6	4
I	11	7	3
Mean	12.8		3.4

a) i) Calculate the mean height of wheat seedlings grown in the solution of pH 5.5. *(2)*

ii) Describe the effect on the growth of the wheat seedlings of being watered with these solutions of different pH. *(2)*

b) This experiment aimed to demonstrate that acid rain can affect plant growth. Outside the classroom, burning of fossil fuels produces a gas that forms sulfuric acid. Name the gas and describe how it could lead to acid rain. *(2)*

c) Some farmers noticed that in one of the lakes near their fields, the water was clear and transparent and there were very few fish. This lake was close to a factory that depended on coal (a fossil fuel) for its fuel supply. The usual direction of the wind and rain in this area blew directly from the factory across the lake. By comparison, lakes much further away from the factory had water that was usually cloudier and these lakes contained more fish.

The farmers thought that the differences in the lakes had something to do with the factory but they did not understand why. Explain to the farmers how their suggestion was probably correct and might lead to what they had noticed in the lake. *(4)*

(Total = 10 marks)

Student 1 response Total 9/10	Marker comments and tips for success
a) i) pH 5.5 60, ✓ = 6.0 O	The student added up the columns correctly but has divided by 10 rather than by 9.
ii) The one with least growth is the one watered with pH 4.5. ✓	By checking the mark allocation (2) the student would have seen that more than one observation was needed for full marks. Comparison of the amount of growth with the pH of the solutions shows a trend: the lower the pH the less the growth.
b) Sulfur dioxide. ✓ The gas dissolves and makes the rain acid. ✓	2 marks
c) The acid rain comes from the factory. O The lakes further away don't get the acid rain so they are normal. The acid in the lake ✓ affects the small organisms and plants ✓ living in the lake. The plants are the producers, so without them the animals die ✓ and there is no food for the fish. ✓	It is sulfur dioxide from the factory that causes acid rain – so not quite enough for a mark. (Marks are never transferred, e.g. from part b).) Student 1 links the acid rain to acid in lakes, then to loss of plants (i.e. the cause of the water becoming clear). A link to 'producers' and animal death is just enough for the 'food webs affected' mark, though this could be explained more fully.

Student 2 response Total 9/10	Marker comments and tips for success
a) i) pH 5.5 60 ÷ 9 ✓ = 6.7 ✓	Correct answer gains 2 marks.
ii) The lower the pH the less the growth. ✓ For example, at pH 5.5 the mean growth is 6.7 cm, but at pH 4.5 the mean is 3.4 cm, i.e. it has only grown half as much ✓ in the same time.	A good description of the effects.
b) Sulfur dioxide. ✓ If there is water in the air the sulfur dioxide dissolves ✓ and when it rains this is called acid rain.	A full answer to the question.
c) When the factory burns coal, sulfur dioxide is produced, and the wind blows it from the factory chimneys across the lake. The gas dissolves in water so the rain in the area near the factory is acid ✓ and that is how it reaches the lake. Eventually the water is so acid ✓ that the organisms in the lake are killed, O including the fish. O The lakes further away are not affected by acid rain.	The link between the factory and acid rain, and the lake water becoming acidic, is explained well. Linking the acidity to the killing of fish is not quite enough for a mark. More detail, such as a description of the effects on gills, would gain this mark. For another mark, the student needed to explain why the water was so clear. If you underline key words when reading the question this may help you focus on what has to be covered in a longer answer.

Practice questions

2 A weather station in Hawaii monitors carbon dioxide concentration in the atmosphere. Data collected there can be used to reflect events occurring on a global scale.

Graph A shows changes in carbon dioxide concentration recorded at this weather station on a monthly basis over a period of one year (February 2012 to February 2013).

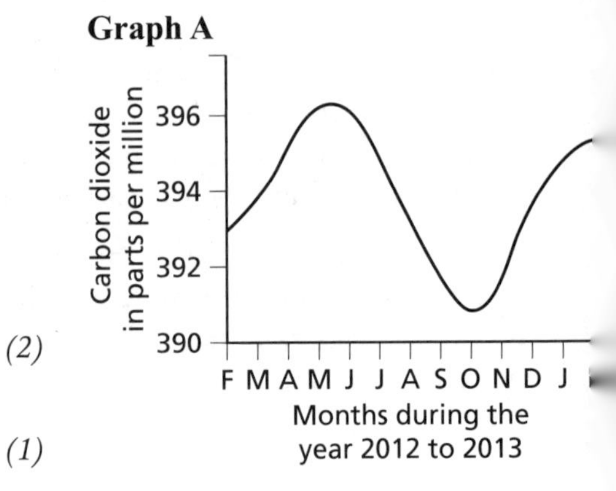

a) i) Give **two** processes that release carbon dioxide into the atmosphere. *(2)*

ii) Which process in green plants uses carbon dioxide from the atmosphere? *(1)*

iii) Suggest why there are fluctuations in carbon dioxide concentration in the atmosphere during the year, as shown in Graph A. *(3)*

b) Graph B shows data for carbon dioxide concentration recorded at this weather station over a period of 5 years, from 2008 to 2013. The blue line shows the average of the fluctuations during each year.

Carbon dioxide is described as a greenhouse gas and contributes to the greenhouse effect.

i) Explain how greenhouse gases contribute to global warming. *(3)*

ii) Name **two** greenhouse gases, other than carbon dioxide and water vapour, and give **one** source of each of the gases you name. *(4)*

Graph B

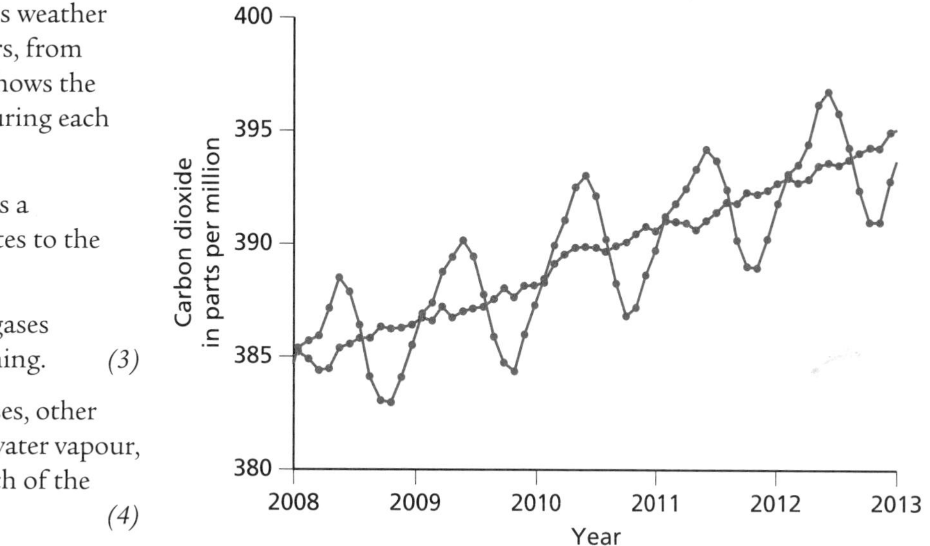

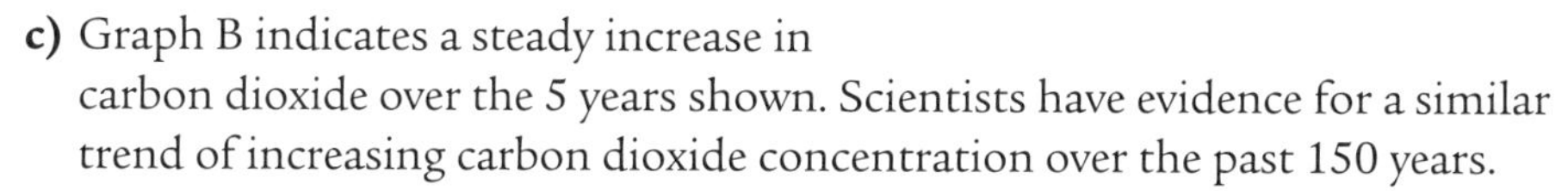

c) Graph B indicates a steady increase in carbon dioxide over the 5 years shown. Scientists have evidence for a similar trend of increasing carbon dioxide concentration over the past 150 years.

Describe how human activities may have contributed to this increase in global carbon dioxide concentration. *(3)*

(Total = 16 marks)

3 The table lists a selection of animals and information about some of the foods they eat. All the animals are found in woods in Europe. Living (green) plants are also present in the woods. Dead plant material, such as dead leaves, is found on the ground in the woods.

Animal	Food the animal might eat
ants	caterpillars, earthworms, earwigs
blue tits	ants, aphids, caterpillars, earwigs
caterpillars	living plants
earthworms	dead plant material
earwigs	dead plant material, living plants
ground beetles	ants, caterpillars, earthworms
robins	ants, caterpillars, earthworms
sparrowhawks	blue tits, robins
tawny owls	earthworms, ground beetles, woodmice
woodmice	nuts, berries, caterpillars, earthworms, earwigs

Use information in the table to answer the questions below.

a) i) Write down **one** food chain with four organisms, including a living plant and a sparrowhawk. Use arrows to show the direction of energy flow. *(3)*

ii) What is the source of energy for organisms in this food chain? *(1)*

b) i) Write down **one** food chain with at least three (living) organisms, including an earthworm (a detritivore) and a tawny owl. *(1)*

ii) Use this food chain to explain how detritivores help to introduce an energy source for organisms in the food chain. *(2)*

c) Explain why feeding relationships are often summarised in a food web rather than a food chain. Use examples in the table to help in your explanation. *(3)*

d) A pyramid of energy represents the energy contained in each trophic level. Explain why a pyramid of energy for a food web always has a wide base and a narrow top. *(3)*

(Total = 13 marks)

Practical activities

Example

1 The diagram shows a pitfall trap. The container is buried in a hole dug into the soil, with the opening level with the surface of the soil. The large stone over the top stops large animals getting in and the small stones round the edge make sure there are gaps that allow small animals to enter.

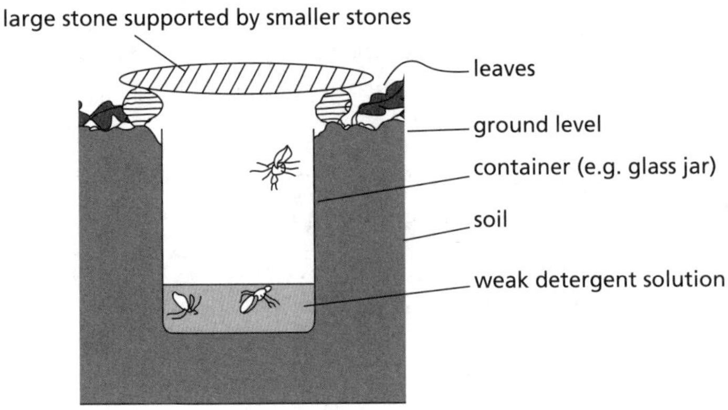

A pitfall trap can be used to find out about small animals in the layer of leaves on the ground. Animals that fall into the trap cannot climb out of the container.

Some students suggested that there might be differences in the invertebrate animals under an oak tree and under a pine tree. They used one pitfall trap under each type of tree and examined the contents of the container after 24 hours. They sorted the animals into groups and counted the number in each group. Their results are given in the table.

a) i) Plot these results in a bar chart so that you can compare them. *(5)*

ii) Calculate the percentage of the total animals caught that were in the trap under the pine tree. Show your working. *(2)*

b) Suggest why they left the traps for 24 hours before examining the contents. *(1)*

c) One student said that the results show that there is a greater abundance and a greater diversity of animals under the oak tree compared with the pine tree. Describe **two** ways that you could modify or extend the investigation to support this suggestion. *(2)*

(Total = 10 marks)

Group of animals	Total number of animals caught in 24 hours	
	Under oak tree	Under pine tree
Beetles	12	10
Springtails	31	5
Spiders	7	2
Harvestmen	6	0
Woodlice	2	3
Slugs	2	0

Student 1 response Total 8/13

a) i)

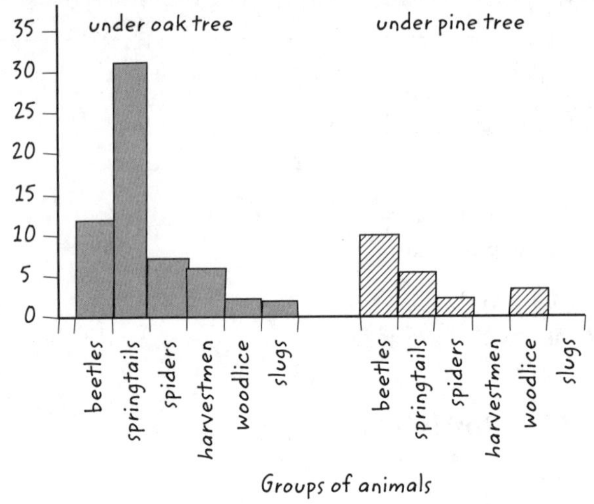

Vertical axis O *Plotting* ✔ *Width of bars* O
Horizontal axis ✔ *Key* ✔

Marker comments and tips for success

The student was asked to draw a bar chart that would provide effective comparison between the results. By plotting the bars in two groups, one for oak and one for pine, some comparison between the two trees is possible. For a clearer visual comparison the bars should be drawn in pairs (see the bar chart drawn by student 2).

It is not necessary to draw the bars with a ruler in the exam, provided the bars are neat, the heights are accurate and the information is clearly conveyed.

The bars of a bar chart should not touch, unlike those of a histogram. There should be a small gap, ideally the same width, between each bar.

To ensure that the bars can be compared fairly, all the bars should be the same width. They could even be represented by a line.

The horizontal axis was correctly labelled, but the vertical axis had no labels. The bars vary in width – they should be the same.

(continued

Student 1 response Total 8/13	Marker comments and tips for success
ii) *Pine tree trap i = 20, oak tree trap = 60.* *Percentage of total animals caught that were in pine tree trap = 20 ÷ 60* O *× 100 = 33%* O	The student added up the numbers in each trap correctly but did not add them together to obtain the total number of animals caught (80). The student used the figure 60, rather than 80, in the calculation, so no marks could be awarded. Calculations like this one are often found on exam papers. Make sure you are clear about which figures to use in a percentage calculation – practice will help.
b) *Some animals only come out at night.* ✔	A reasonable suggestion.
c) *You could put some more pitfall traps out under the oak and pine trees.* ✔ *You could leave the traps out for a longer time.* ✔	2 marks (just). Think carefully about your ideas and try to think of some practical details. What is meant by 'a longer time' – two days, two weeks?

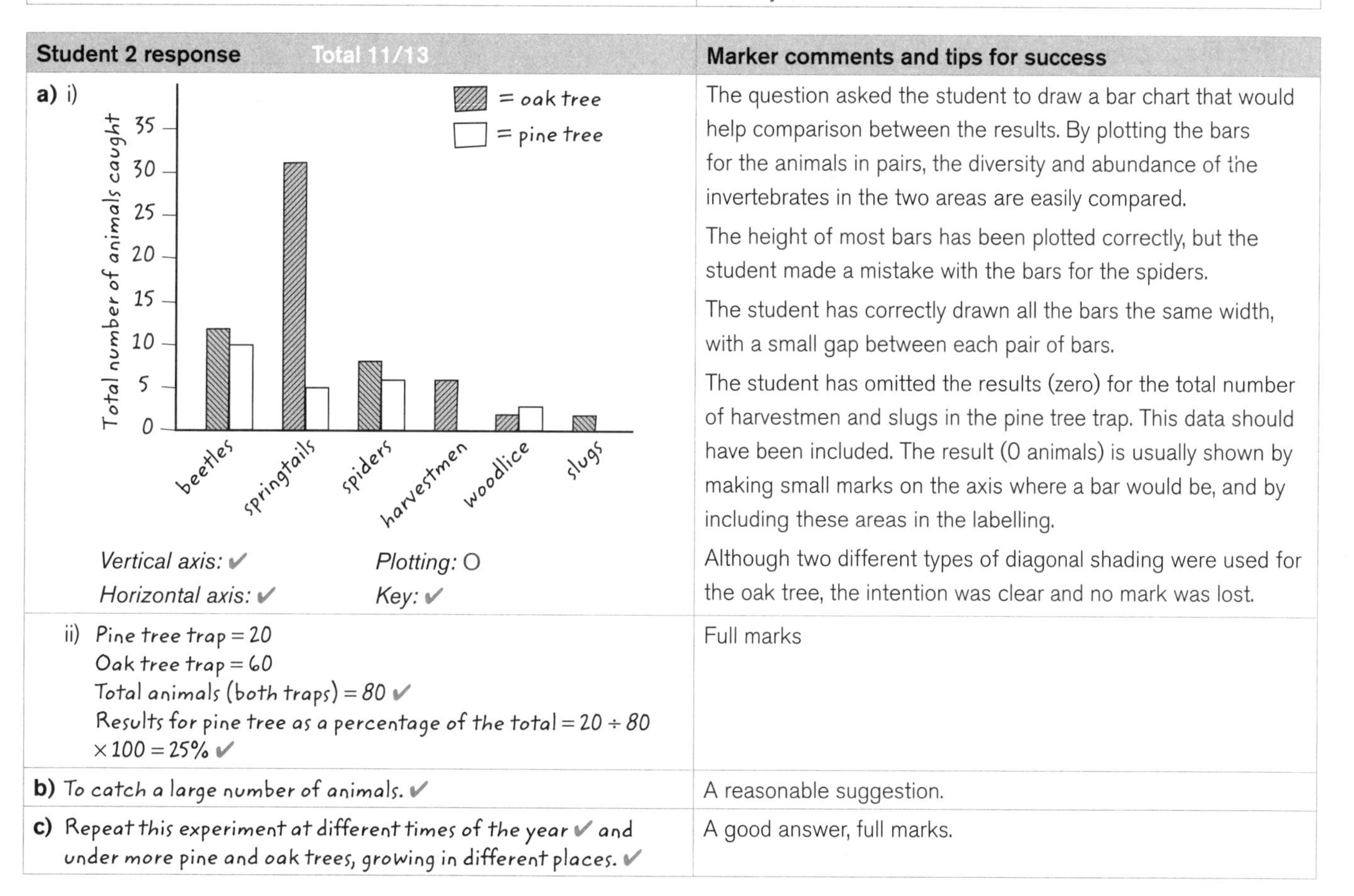

Student 2 response Total 11/13	Marker comments and tips for success
a) i) 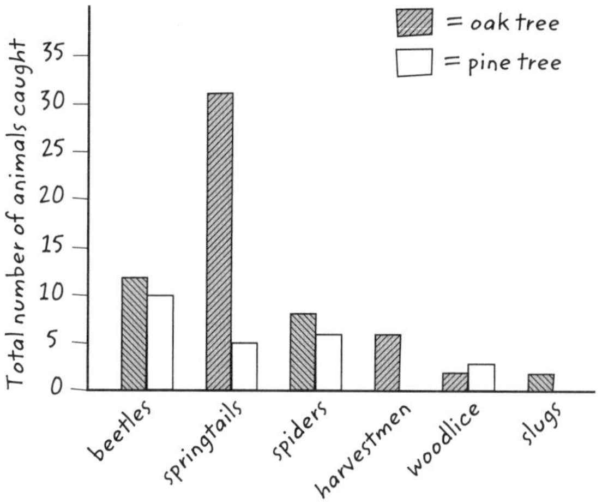 *Vertical axis:* ✔ *Plotting:* O *Horizontal axis:* ✔ *Key:* ✔	The question asked the student to draw a bar chart that would help comparison between the results. By plotting the bars for the animals in pairs, the diversity and abundance of the invertebrates in the two areas are easily compared. The height of most bars has been plotted correctly, but the student made a mistake with the bars for the spiders. The student has correctly drawn all the bars the same width, with a small gap between each pair of bars. The student has omitted the results (zero) for the total number of harvestmen and slugs in the pine tree trap. This data should have been included. The result (0 animals) is usually shown by making small marks on the axis where a bar would be, and by including these areas in the labelling. Although two different types of diagonal shading were used for the oak tree, the intention was clear and no mark was lost.
ii) *Pine tree trap = 20* *Oak tree trap = 60* *Total animals (both traps) = 80* ✔ *Results for pine tree as a percentage of the total = 20 ÷ 80 × 100 = 25%* ✔	Full marks
b) *To catch a large number of animals.* ✔	A reasonable suggestion.
c) *Repeat this experiment at different times of the year* ✔ *and under more pine and oak trees, growing in different places.* ✔	A good answer, full marks.

Practice questions

2 Daisy plants have small white flowers and they are easily seen and recognised in areas of short grass.

Some students noticed that daisies were growing in two different areas of grass in their school grounds. Students often walked across one of the areas (area A) on their way to different buildings in the school so they had trampled on the grass in this area. The other area (area B) was out of the way and people rarely walked there.

The students decided to compare the effect of trampling on the distribution of daises in these two areas. They used a quadrat (0.5 × 0.5 m) to sample each area. They counted the number of daisies in the quadrats. They recorded the number of daisies in 10 quadrats in each of the areas. Their results are shown in the table on the next page.

Quadrat number	Total number of daisy flowers in each quadrat	
	Area A (trampled)	Area B (not trampled)
1	0	7
2	15	4
3	8	11
4	12	7
5	5	3
6	10	6
7	9	5
8	2	3
9	16	8
10	9	9
Totals		63

a) The total number of daisies counted in area B (the untrampled area) is given in the table.

i) Calculate the total number of daisies in area A (the trampled area). *(1)*

ii) The density of daisy flowers in area A is 344 per m^2. Calculate the density of daisy flowers in area B. *(2)*

b) i) How has trampling affected the number of daisy plants in these grass areas? *(1)*

ii) Suggest why trampling may have influenced the number of daisy flowers in the two areas. *(2)*

c) When doing the investigation, the students used a random method for placing the quadrats.

i) Explain why the students used quadrats in their investigation. *(2)*

ii) Why is it important to use a random method for placing the quadrats? *(1)*

iii) Describe how the quadrats could be placed randomly. *(2)*

d) i) Area A (trampled grass) shows more variation than area B (untrampled grass) in the number of daisy flowers per quadrat. Suggest a reason for this. *(1)*

ii) Suggest **two** factors other than trampling that may have influenced the presence of daisy flowers in each area. *(2)*

(Total = 14 marks)

3 Some students investigated the growth of organisms on the trunks of trees growing in a wood in a damp area.

They recognised four types of organisms growing on the tree trunks: algae, foliose (leafy) lichens, crustose (flat) lichens and moss.

The students compared the growth of these organisms on two species of tree growing in the wood: ash and sycamore. They used quadrats with a grid inside the quadrat and made an estimate of percentage cover of these organisms on the trunks of several trees. If there was nothing growing, they recorded bare bark. The quadrat on a tree trunk is shown in the diagram.

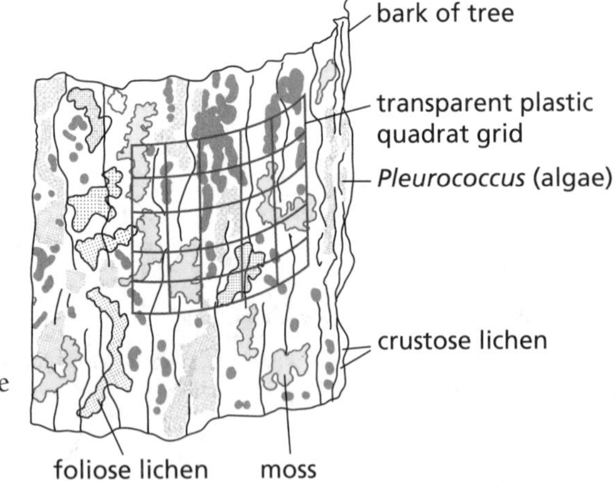

Their combined results from several trees are shown in the pie charts.

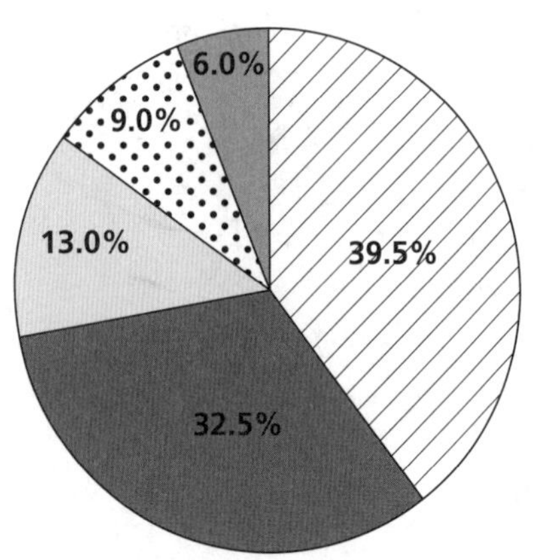

Percentage cover of species on ash tree bark

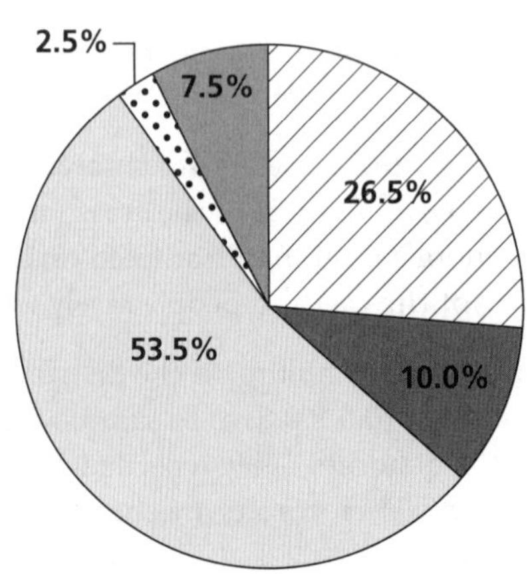

Percentage cover of species on sycamore tree bark

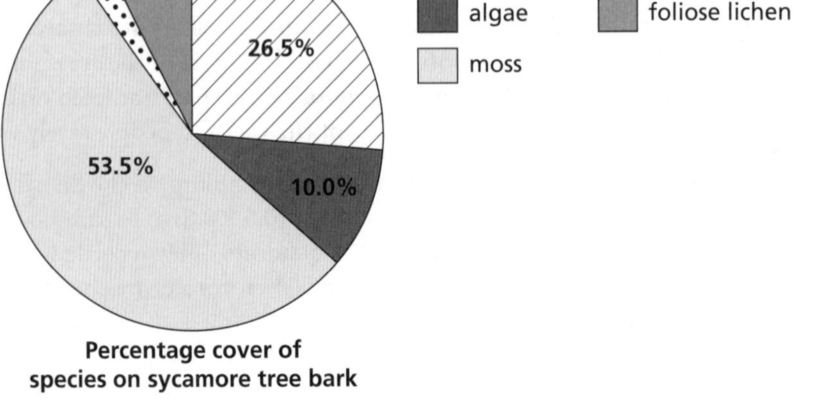

a) i) When collecting their data, suggest why the students used several trees of each species. *(1)*

ii) Suggest the advantage of using quadrats with a grid inside. *(1)*

iii) Give **one** variable the students should control when using the quadrats and give a reason for your answer. *(2)*

b) Two students decided to present the results in a bar chart rather than in a pie chart.

i) Draw a bar chart so that you can compare percentage cover of each category of organism recorded on these trees. *(5)*

ii) From this investigation, which species of tree showed greatest variation in cover of the different organisms growing on the trunk? Use figures from the results to support your answer. *(2)*

c) The students knew that algae are protoctists and learnt that lichens are an association between an alga and a fungus growing together. Mosses are simple plants that lack xylem and grow only to a small size.

i) Which of the organisms listed above contains no chlorophyll? Suggest how this organism obtains its food supply. *(2)*

ii) Suggest why moss plants grow only to a small size. *(2)*

(Total = 15 marks)

4 *Pleurococcus* is an alga (a Protoctist) that often grows on the bark of trees. It forms a film and when it is dry it looks like a green powder. *Pleurococcus* is single-celled, contains chlorophyll and requires light and moisture to carry out photosynthesis.

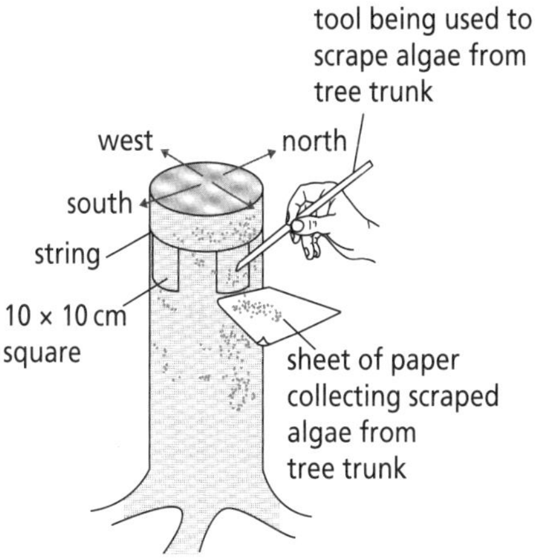

Some students investigated the abundance of *Pleurococcus* on different sides of the trunk of a tree. They lived in an area where the prevailing winds carrying rain blow from the west. They predicted that the alga would grow best on the west side of a tree trunk and less well on the north and south sides.

They chose three ash trees (A, B and C) and tied a string around each tree at a height of 120 cm. On three sides of each tree (north, south and west), they marked an area 10 cm × 10 cm just above the string. They scraped the *Pleurococcus* off the bark from inside each of these areas into pieces of folded paper. This is shown in the diagram.

To estimate the quantity of *Pleurococcus* in each area, they transferred the powder collected in each paper into a boiling tube containing 10 cm^3 of ethanol (alcohol). They placed the boiling tubes in a boiling water bath for 2 minutes. The ethanol in each tube became green as the chlorophyll pigments were extracted from the algae. The intensity of the green colour in the ethanol was matched with a colour chart and scored as 0 (colourless) to 10 (very green).

The table shows their results.

Direction faced by side of tree	Colour score of green extract		
	Tree A	Tree B	Tree C
North	2	0	3
South	1	0	2
West	5	4	5

a) i) How many safety boiling tubes of ethanol with *Pleurococcus* samples did they place in the boiling water bath? *(1)*

ii) Describe **one** safety precaution they took when carrying out this investigation and explain why the precaution was taken. *(2)*

b) i) How far do their results support their predictions? Use figures in the table to support your answer. *(3)*

ii) Suggest why they predicted more algal growth on the west side of the trees. *(3)*

iii) How could they make their results more reliable? *(1)*

(Total = 10 marks)

Applying principles

Example

1 The food web shows some feeding relationships for marine organisms living in polar seas. Phytoplankton is made up of microscopic organisms that can carry out photosynthesis, including many algae.

a) Use organisms shown in the food web to complete the table. Organisms may be used once, more than once or not at all. *(3)*

Description	Name of organism
one group of organisms that are producers	
two organisms that are both primary and secondary consumers	
two organisms that are tertiary consumers	

b) i) Explain what is meant by **biomass**. *(1)*

ii) Which group of organisms has the greatest biomass in this food web during the whole year? *(1)*

c) A region of the polar seas, with organisms in this food web, suffers from pesticide pollution. The pesticide is not biodegradable (does not break down quickly). An analysis of samples of tissues from organisms in this food web showed the highest concentration in the killer whale. Suggest an explanation for this. *(2)*

d) Fishing of cod increased in the region until it became 'unsustainable'. This means that the fish (cod) were removed at a faster rate than they could be replaced by natural breeding.

If cod became extinct as a result of over-fishing, predict and explain **two** ways that this might affect the food web. *(2)*

e) Polar regions have a good supply of mineral ions, carried in sea currents, such as the Gulf Stream.

i) Which group of organisms benefits directly from this supply of mineral ions? *(1)*

ii) Suggest **two** mineral ions that are important for this group. *(2)*

(Total = 12 marks)

Student 1 response Total 9/12	Marker comments and tips for success
a) *zooplankton* O *cod and squid* O *killer whale and leopard seal* ✓	Zooplankton are animals (the 'zoo' in the name might help you) so are not the producers. You should be able to interpret food webs based on unfamiliar ecosystems. In the question you are told that phytoplankton carry out photosynthesis so this gives you the clue that they are producers. To help identify the producers, look for an organism with no arrow pointing towards it (so does not feed on other organisms). Cod is correct, but not squid.
b) i) *The mass of all living organisms at a stage of a food chain.* ✓	Correct response.
ii) *The killer whale.* O	Although each killer whale is a large animal, the biomass of the tertiary (and quaternary) consumers at the top of the pyramid of biomass is very small compared with the biomass of the producers at the bottom.

(continued)

Student 1 response Total 9/12	Marker comments and tips for success
c) The killer whale is at the top of the food chain. The pesticide is taken into the bodies of the small animals at the bottom of the food chain and when they are eaten by the food of the killer whale, ✔ the whale gets a high dose of pesticide. It has accumulated through the food chain. ✔	The student gains a mark for describing the way that the pesticide is passed up through the food chain to the whale. The second mark is for describing the accumulation of the pesticide, plus the description 'high dose of pesticide' for the whale.
d) There would be less food for the leopard seals, which at present eat cod, squid and penguins, so their numbers would go down. ✔ The krill would no longer be eaten by the cod, so their population would probably go up. ✔	The disappearance of cod from the food web would affect many of the organisms. Student 1 has given a good description of two possible outcomes.
e) i) The plants in the sea, such as plankton, ✔ need minerals.	Student 1 applied knowledge learned during the course to the unfamiliar marine food web – i.e. that algae, like green plants, carry out photosynthesis and also need a supply of mineral ions. Strictly speaking, algae are not plants, but the student's answer is accepted for the mark.
ii) Nitrate ✔ for growth and magnesium ✔ for making chlorophyll.	Answer is correct but some students mistakenly refer to 'nitrogen' rather than nitrate. The only times it is correct to refer to 'nitrogen' is in the context of nitrogen gas, or as a molecule (e.g. describing the nitrogen cycle or amino acid structure).

Student 2 response Total 12/12	Marker comments and tips for success
a) phytoplankton ✔ cod and krill ✔ penguin and leopard seal ✔	To find organisms that were both primary and secondary consumers, the student looked for organisms that were the first consumers in one food chain and the second consumers in another. e.g. phytoplankton → krill phytoplankton → zooplankton → krill
b) i) Biomass is the total mass of living organisms in e.g. a wood. ✔	A clear answer.
ii) The producers. ✔	Correct answer.
c) The pesticide is taken in from the water by the producers and passes to the primary and secondary consumers, going up the food chain to the killer whale. ✔ The pesticide doesn't break down ✔ (it is not biodegradable) so it stays poisonous and builds up to dangerous levels (✔).	The student applied understanding of food chains to the information about the pesticide (not biodegradable) in the question. She could have gained a third mark for saying the pesticide builds up in the killer whale, but the maximum for the question had been reached.
d) There would be more zooplankton because they would not be eaten by cod. ✔ There would be more squid, as more food (zooplankton) for them. ✔	Full marks for a good description of two possible outcomes if cod became extinct.
e) i) The phytoplankton. ✔ They are the producers in the food web and like all green plants they need mineral salts e.g. magnesium.	Do not waste time by writing more than is necessary. Always check the mark allocation to judge how much information is expected. As advised for student 1, strictly speaking algae are not plants, but the student has already answered the question and this part of the answer is not needed.
ii) Magnesium ✔ and phosphates ✔	In this question, any correct answer is given credit, even if it is based on knowledge beyond that required by the specification (e.g. phosphate).

Practice questions

2 A river flows through a village. As a result of building work, a sewage pipe was accidentally broken and some untreated sewage entered the river.

The graph shows the number of bacteria in the water at different distances along the river. The untreated sewage entered at point S. The graph on the next page also shows changes in the levels of oxygen in the water as a result of the entry of sewage.

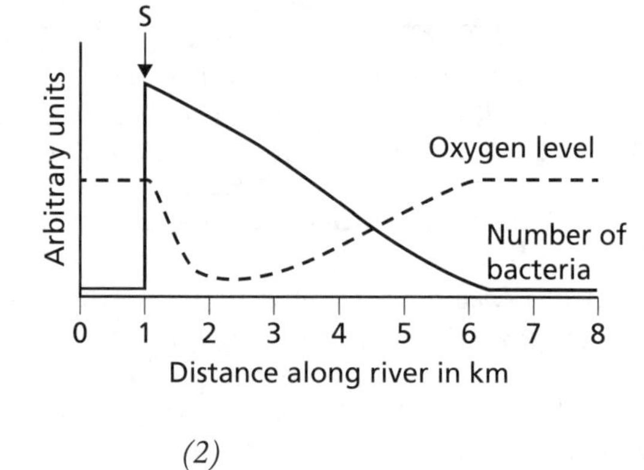

a) The sewage contains a high level of bacteria and is also rich in mineral ions.

i) Explain why there is a sharp fall in oxygen level, after the entry of the sewage, between 1 and 2 km along the river. *(3)*

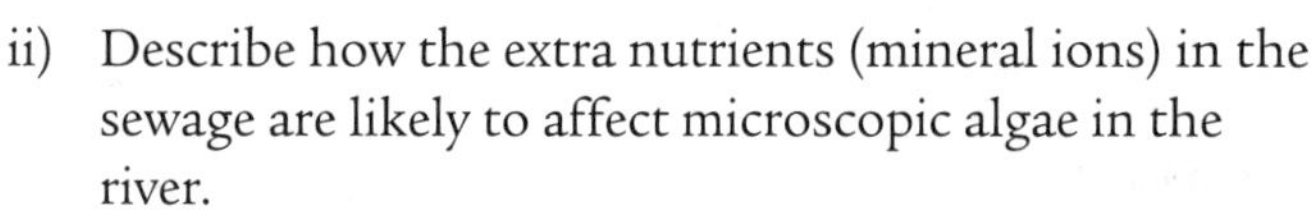

ii) Describe how the extra nutrients (mineral ions) in the sewage are likely to affect microscopic algae in the river. *(2)*

iii) Suggest why the oxygen level rises again after 3 km along the river. *(2)*

b) If entry of the sewage became a permanent feature in this river, suggest how this might affect other organisms, including fish, in the river close to the point S. Give reasons for your answers. *(3)*

(Total = 10 marks)

3 Lichens are small organisms that are an association between an alga and a fungus growing together. Lichens are sensitive to air pollution and certain species do not grow well in polluted areas. Because of this, lichens are sometimes used as indicators of the level of pollution.

The map shows part of the UK (England and Wales). The coloured squares represent the abundance of lichens found on ash trees.

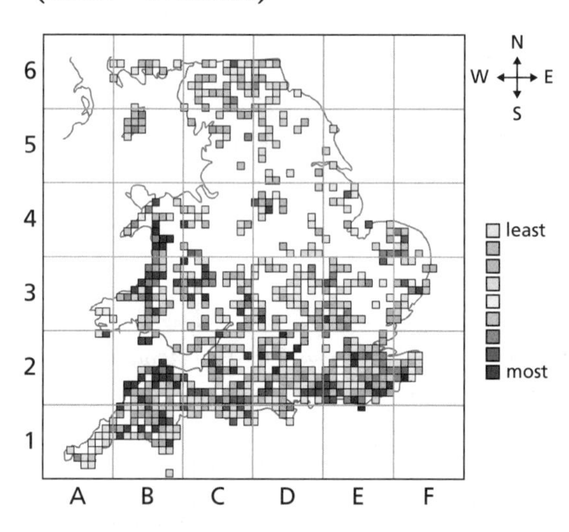

a) Large cities and industrial areas are usually major sources of air pollution.

i) On the map, identify **two** areas where there is evidence of a high level of air pollution. Use squares on the grid to show the areas you choose. Each square can be linked to the letters and numbers on the axes. *(2)*

ii) Name **one** gas that is likely to be produced in industrial areas that causes air pollution. *(1)*

iii) Explain how this gas can affect the rain that falls in the area. *(2)*

b) In the UK, the most common winds bringing rain come from the west and south-west. What evidence is there in the map to indicate that this has influenced the distribution of lichens? *(2)*

c) i) Which component of a lichen is able to carry out photosynthesis? *(1)*

ii) Write down a list of what the lichen requires to carry out photosynthesis and synthesise carbohydrates. This can be shown in a word equation. *(3)*

d) Many lichens grow on tree trunks, rocks and stone walls, where there is no soil. They can often survive in areas with extremes of humidity and temperature.

i) Suggest how lichens obtain their supplies of mineral ions. *(1)*

ii) Suggest why lichens are often important in colonising areas of bare rock leading to the establishment of a community of plants and animals. *(3)*

(Total = 15 marks)

Extended writing

Example

1 Explain how deforestation can cause flooding and affect the fertility of the soil in the deforested area. *(6)*

Student 1 response
Forests are cut down so that people can build houses and roads. The bulldozers disturb the soil when they take the trees away. The soil can get washed down the hill into the rivers. If the river gets blocked there might be some flooding somewhere else. When there are fewer trees there is less photosynthesis so less carbon dioxide is removed. This helps global warming.
Student 2 response
When trees are cut down the soil is easily eroded. Nutrients are also washed out of the soil so it is less fertile. If there aren't any trees the leaves don't fall to the ground and so the bacteria in the soil don't break them down and release the nutrients. Sometimes there is flooding because the trees don't take up the water and it stays in the ground.
Mark scheme
The mark scheme shows how marks are awarded. (1) vegetation / soil on ground exposed / no longer protected by trees / eq (2) less water taken up by trees from soil / eq (3) water can run off more easily (if on slope) / eq (4) (vegetation) does not bind / hold soil / eq (5) soil eroded / washed away / eq (6) (washed away soil) accumulates in rivers / blocks waterways in valleys (leading to flooding) / eq (7) soil can become saturated (because trees do not take up the water), leading to flooding / eq (8) mineral ion content (of soil) washed away / removed / leaching / eq (9) microorganisms (in soil) washed away / eq (10) (therefore) disturbance to soil recycling / eq (11) less vegetation on surface / eq that would break down / decompose / eq (12) mineral ions / eq not released from decaying vegetation / eq (13) soil less fertile / eq Total: 6

Student 1 response Total 2/6	Marker comments and tips for success
Forests are cut down so that people can build houses and roads.	No marks. This was not asked for in the question.
The bulldozers disturb the soil when they take the trees away. The soil can get washed down the hill into the rivers. ✓	No marks for the first sentence but 'washed down the hill' is enough for mark (5).
If the river gets blocked there might be some flooding somewhere else. ✓	This links flooding with rivers getting blocked and gains mark (6).
When there are fewer trees there is less photosynthesis so less carbon dioxide is removed. This helps global warming.	The statements are correct but do not answer the question set. Always read the question carefully and select relevant information for your response.

Student 2 response Total 6/6	Marker comments and tips for success
When trees are cut down the soil is easily eroded. ✓	Student 2 gains mark (5) with correct use of the term 'eroded'.
Nutrients are also washed out ✓ *of the soil so it is less fertile.* ✓	The first sentence gains marks (8) and (13). 'Nutrients' is an acceptable alternative (as 'eq') to 'mineral ions'.
If there aren't any trees the leaves don't fall to the ground and so the bacteria in the soil don't break them down and release the nutrients. ✓	Several points contribute to mark (11) but no mark for mention of bacteria (9), as this is awarded only in the context of being washed away. Student 2 correctly links less vegetation on the soil with being broken down (or decomposed).
Sometimes there is flooding because the trees don't take up the water ✓ *and it stays in the ground.* ✓	'Trees don't take up the water' earns mark (2). No mark for mention of 'flooding' as this is in the question but it is correctly linked to water in the ground, equivalent to mark (7).

Extended writing questions – general advice

The list summarises the skills being tested and how to approach your answers to this type of question. You should read this advice and also look at the mark scheme for the particular question you are doing, together with the guidance for students to help you understand the mark scheme.

- Skills being tested include the ability to select and organise information.
- Facts must be correct and relevant to the question. For example, in this question on deforestation, student 1 had given some correct information (at the beginning and at the end) but these statements did not answer any part of the question set.
- Often a single word is not enough for a mark but requires further description or elaboration in some way.
- The question may expect you to make links between different aspects of a topic, so make sure those links are clear in what you write. For example, in this question on deforestation, several of the mark points need to be correctly linked – the relevant 'link' ideas are usually given in brackets in the mark scheme so you must make sure the context is clear.
- The question may refer to two different parts of a topic – say, features or processes to compare. Make sure you cover both aspects, otherwise you will not be able to gain full marks.
- No marks are awarded for the quality of written work (such as spelling, grammar and organisation of subject matter), but you are more likely to include all the relevant material if you organise it sensibly and logically. It is also easier for the examiner to read if your handwriting is legible and written in sentences that are clearly set out.
- Sometimes you may decide it is useful to draw a diagram to help with your answer. If you do this, make sure the diagram is labelled, or annotated with notes, so that it can be understood and links in with the rest of your written answer.
- The mark allocation is usually 6 marks. This gives a guide as to how long you spend on this question in relation to the rest of the paper (probably about 6 minutes). Use your time sensibly by jotting down a brief plan or a list of what you want to include as this will help you select and organise the material better and gain more marks for your answer. If you have 6 minutes, you can spend about 3 minutes planning and deciding what you are going to write. Then 3 minutes is enough to write an answer that gains full marks.

Practice questions

2 A pyramid of energy is a way of representing the total energy contained in the organisms in a community. Explain why a pyramid of energy is wide at the base but becomes progressively narrower with each trophic level towards the top. *(6)*

3 Describe the part played by microorganisms in the carbon cycle and in the nitrogen cycle. *(6)*

4 A person running across grassland uses the process of respiration to release energy from glucose in the leg muscles. Describe how a carbon atom in a glucose molecule in the runner's leg can become part of a muscle in a rabbit, an animal that is a primary consumer and lives in the surrounding grassland. *(6)*

7 Use of biological resources

Using and interpreting data

Example

1 Radishes are plants in the cabbage family. As the plant grows, the roots swell. These roots are often eaten as a vegetable.

An investigation was carried out in a school laboratory into the effect of fertiliser containing different concentrations of nitrogen on the growth of radish plants.

The radishes were grown in small plastic pots, as shown in the diagram. Each nutrient solution was identical except for different levels of nitrogen (supplied as potassium nitrate). The pots were kept in the light throughout the investigation.

One radish seed was pushed into the sand in each pot. After 18 days the radishes were harvested. Each plant was removed from the pot and washed carefully in water to remove any sand. The plants were then separated into the tops (leaves) and roots. Each part was dried at 110 °C for 24 hours and weighed to obtain the dry mass. The results for all the plants (from 18 pots) at each nitrogen concentration were combined and a mean value was calculated.

The results for the whole plants and for the roots only are shown in the graph.

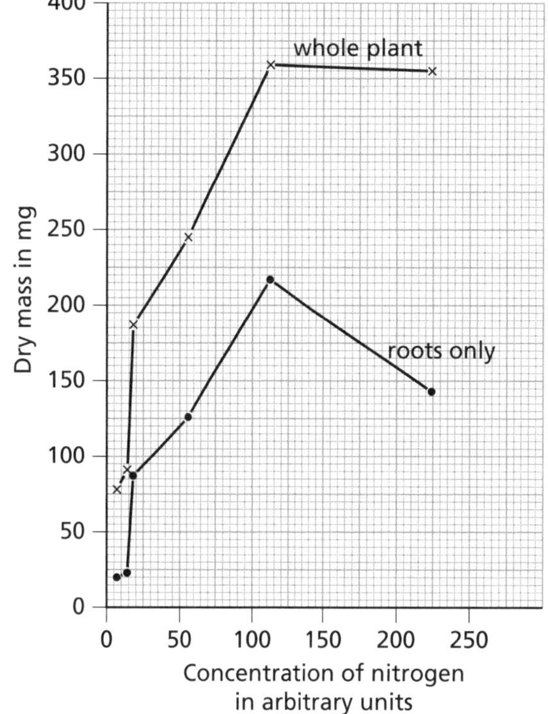

a) i) In this investigation, what was the highest dry mass of whole radish plants obtained and at what concentration of nitrogen? *(2)*

ii) Describe the effect of nitrogen concentration on the growth of roots compared with the growth of the whole plants. Make reference to similarities and differences shown in the patterns of growth. *(3)*

b) The table shows the percentage of the dry mass of the whole plant that was found in the leaves at each nitrogen concentration. Note that the percentage dry mass for a nitrogen concentration of 112 arbitrary units is missing from the table.

Nitrogen concentration in arbitrary units	7	14	28	56	112	224
Percentage of dry mass in leaves at harvest (%)	74.0	75.0	53.0	48.5		59.7

i) Use information in the graph to calculate the percentage dry mass in the leaves grown at a nitrogen concentration of 112 arbitrary units. Show your working. *(3)*

ii) What does the investigation show about the proportion of material in the leaves of plants of different sizes (compare smaller plants with larger plants)? *(2)*

c) A grower needs to encourage good root growth to obtain a high yield of radishes to sell in a local market. From the results of this investigation, what advice would you give to the grower? *(2)*

(Total = 12 marks)

Student 1 response Total 0/12	Marker comments and tips for success
a) i) 360 O	Student 1 read the value correctly from the graph but did not give units, so did not get a mark. No value given for the concentration of nitrogen, so student did not gain the second mark. Always check that you have answered all parts within a question.
ii) It rises then it quickly falls again. O	Student 1 does not make it clear what 'it' refers to – whether the reference is to roots or to the whole plant. If the student had said 'roots', there would have been 1 mark for this statement. You should read the question carefully – if it refers to a comparison, make sure you say something about both items. Here the question asks for 'similarities' and 'differences' so you should cover both aspects in your answer.
b) i) for percentage × 100 O	Not enough to gain a mark. Student 1 should read figures from the graph for the dry mass of the whole plant and for the roots. The difference gives the dry mass of the leaves. This value is then used to calculate the percentage dry mass in the leaves.
ii) Bigger plants have bigger roots than smaller plants. O	The question asks about how much of the mass is in the leaves and whether this is different in plants of different sizes. Student 1's answer makes no reference to leaves.
c) Use 112 units of nitrogen O	This value may have been correct for this investigation but would not be the same for crops grown in the field in quite different conditions.

Student 2 response Total 9/12	Marker comments and tips for success
a) i) 355 mg O at 112 nitrogen units ✓	Student 2 has misread the scale but does give the units (for dry mass). The value for nitrogen is correct and 'units' is acceptable here. You should check the scale carefully – every graph is different, and here two squares (on the vertical axis) represented 10 mg (dry mass).
ii) Both roots and whole plant growth are stimulated ✓ by nitrogen, up to a point, but after that point the roots seem to shrink ✓ whilst the whole plant seems to stay still. ✓	Student 2 makes three correct points so gains full marks. (Often more marks are available than the total for the question part.) 'Shrink' is just acceptable for 'less'. 'Up to a point' is a bit vague and you are advised to quote figures where possible to help support your answer.
b) i) Roots = 217 ✓ so leaves = 355 – 217 = 138 mg ✓ % difference = 138 ÷ 355 × 100 = 38.9% ✓	Student 2 has approached the calculation sensibly, by reading the values for whole plants and roots from the graph, then subtracting the roots from the whole plant to find the dry mass of the leaves. Student 2 next worked out the percentage of the plant contained in the leaves. However, Student 2 had already made an error in reading from the graph in (a)(i), but examiners do not penalise you twice for the same error. So marks were awarded even though an incorrect value (for whole plant dry mass) had been used. This emphasises the importance of showing your working in calculations. If student 2 had not shown working, the answer would not have gained any marks.
ii) The bigger plants have a greater proportion of their mass in the form of roots than smaller plants. ✓	A correct interpretation and is acceptable for 1 mark (though the mark scheme presents it the other way round).
c) Use 112 units of nitrogen because this gives you the biggest percentage of dry mass in the roots, ✓ as opposed to the leaves.	Student 2 makes an attempt to give a reason in terms of wanting to have the biggest percentage of dry mass in the roots. As for student 1, the value of 112 units of nitrogen is likely to be quite different when growing the crop in the field. Even though this answer is not exactly as given in the mark scheme, it is accepted as 'eq'.

Practice questions

2 When fruits, such as apples or bananas, are harvested, certain living processes continue, even though the fruit has been removed from the plant.

Commercial fruit growers store the harvested fruit for several weeks (or months) before it is sold in shops and markets. During this time, as the fruits ripen, they may lose weight, change in colour, texture and flavour. The grower aims to ensure that the stored fruits remain in good condition for sale and to minimise losses from fruit that has gone bad (spoiled).

Inside the storage containers, humidity, temperature and the composition of the atmosphere can often be controlled. Different ways of packaging fruits also help to keep them in a suitable condition.

An investigation was carried out into the effect of different wrapping and packaging materials on plantains (a type of banana). They were stored at tropical temperatures (around 30 °C) and in a relative humidity between 60% and 80%. The results of the investigation are summarised in the table.

Packaging materials	Time to ripeness in days	Loss in mass at ripeness compared with mass at harvest (%)
not wrapped	15.8	17.0
paper	18.9	17.9
perforated polythene	26.5	7.2
polythene	36.1	2.6

Note that perforated polythene has many tiny holes.

a) i) Plot these results as a bar chart on a graph grid. Use one vertical axis for 'Time to ripeness in days' and the other vertical axis for 'Loss in mass at ripeness (%)'. *(6)*

ii) Describe the effects of different packaging on the length of time it takes for the plantains to ripen. Use examples in the table to support your answer. *(2)*

b) i) Name **two** processes that would continue in the plantains after harvest and are likely to lead to a loss in mass. In each case, name the substance(s) that would be lost from the plantains. *(2)*

ii) Which type of packaging was least successful in reducing the loss of mass? Suggest why this packaging was not effective. *(2)*

c) Suggest **two** reasons why fruit may become spoiled during storage so that it is unsuitable for sale. *(2)*

d) On the basis of this investigation, what advice would you give to a fruit grower who produced fruit on a small scale and wanted to keep the fruit in good condition as long as possible? *(1)*

(Total = 15 marks)

3 *Lactobacillus* bacteria are involved in a number of fermentations. Yoghurt is made by the fermentation of milk and *Lactobacillus* bacteria are involved in the fermentation process.

Silage is made by the fermentation of grass. Different *Lactobacillus* bacteria are involved in the fermentation process. Making silage preserves grass so that animals (such as cattle) can feed on the silage a year or more after the grass is cut.

In both fermentations, lactic acid is produced from sugars present in the milk and in the grass. The quality of the silage is better if the fermentation takes place quickly.

When making silage, farmers often add a mixture containing bacteria, including *Lactobacillus*, to help speed up the fermentation process. A comparison was made of the effect of adding the mixture with *Lactobacillus* to a sample of grass. A was the control grass sample, without added *Lactobacillus* and B was the grass sample with added *Lactobacillus*.

Graph 1 shows pH changes over a period of 30 days of grass being converted to silage with and without the addition of the bacterial mixture. Graph 2 shows the production of lactic acid in the same fermentation.

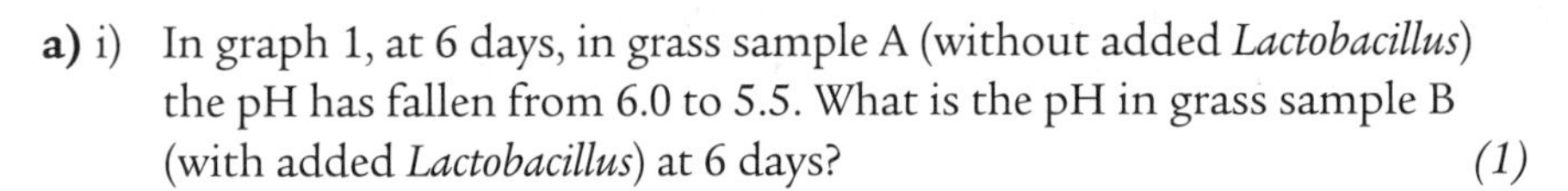

a) i) In graph 1, at 6 days, in grass sample A (without added *Lactobacillus*) the pH has fallen from 6.0 to 5.5. What is the pH in grass sample B (with added *Lactobacillus*) at 6 days? *(1)*

ii) In graph 2, calculate the difference in lactic acid production in grass A (without added *Lactobacillus*) and grass B (with added *Lactobacillus*) at 6 days. Show your working. *(3)*

b) i) Give evidence from the graph to support the view that the fall in pH during the fermentation is the result of the production of lactic acid. *(2)*

ii) In the fermentation of milk for production of yoghurt, how does the fall in pH affect how thick the milk is? *(1)*

c) Making silage is a way of preserving cut grass over a long period of time as food for cattle. Give **two** reasons why yoghurt is produced as a food for humans. *(2)*

d) i) Why does some fermentation occur in grass sample A, when no *Lactobacillus* bacteria are added? *(1)*

ii) Suggest why farmers often cut grass for silage on a sunny day and in the afternoon. *(2)*

(Total = 12 marks)

pH

Time in days

Graph 1

Key
× control (A)
• with mixture of *Lactobacillus* bacteria (B)

Lactic acid concentration in arbitrary units

Time in days

Graph 2

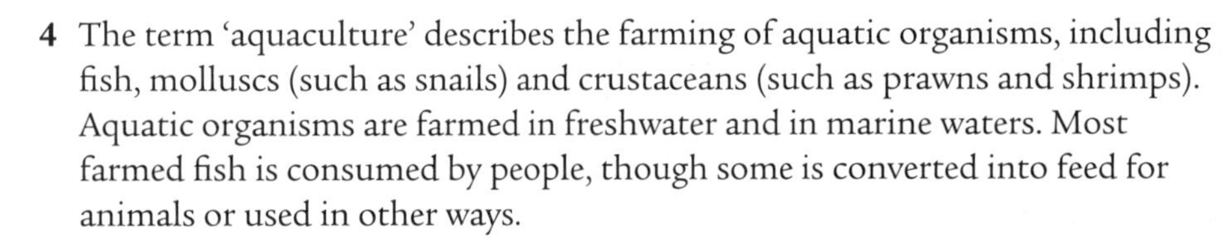

4 The term 'aquaculture' describes the farming of aquatic organisms, including fish, molluscs (such as snails) and crustaceans (such as prawns and shrimps). Aquatic organisms are farmed in freshwater and in marine waters. Most farmed fish is consumed by people, though some is converted into feed for animals or used in other ways.

The table shows the world aquaculture production for 10 years, from 2000 to 2010. Figures show mass of farmed aquatic organisms in millions of tonnes.

Year	Mass in millions of tonnes		
	FW	Marine	Total
2001	21.8	12.8	34.6
2002	23.3	13.5	36.7
2003	24.9	14.0	38.9
2004	27.2	14.7	41.9
2005	29.1	15.2	44.3
2006	31.3	16.0	47.3
2007	33.4	16.6	49.9
2008	36.0	16.9	52.9
2009	38.1	17.6	55.7
2010	41.7	18.1	59.9

a) Describe the changes shown in total aquaculture production over the 10 years from 2001 to 2010. *(1)*

b) i) On a graph grid, plot a line graph to show the data for both freshwater (FW) and marine aquaculture production over the years 2001 to 2010. Plot both sets of data on the same grid. Use a ruler to join the points with straight lines. *(6)*

ii) In 2001, aquaculture production in freshwater was 63% of the total production. Calculate the percentage production in freshwater in 2010. Show your working. *(2)*

iii) Suggest reasons for any changes shown by these graphs over the years 2001 to 2010. *(2)*

c) i) Suggest **two** advantages of producing fish by aquaculture rather than catching wild fish. *(2)*

ii) Describe **two** ways in which aquaculture may harm the environment. *(2)*

(Total = 15 marks)

Practical activities

Example

1 Some students investigated the effect of temperature on respiration in yeast. They were provided with a mixture containing 4 g of yeast and 20 g of sugar in 200 cm^3 of water. This had been mixed thoroughly.

The students used a pipette to transfer 10 cm^3 of the mixture into a set of test tubes. They were careful to ensure that no foam formed on the surface as they did this. They then placed pairs of test tubes in water baths set at different temperatures. The range of temperatures is shown in the table.

After 30 minutes in the water baths, the students removed the test tubes. They measured the height of the foam that had developed above the surface of the liquid. Their results are shown in the table.

Temperature in °C	Height of foam above surface of liquid in mm	
	Tube 1	Tube 2
20	3	4
30	5	5
40	20	8
50	23	29
60	15	10
70	3	4

a) i) Suggest why a gas has been given off, causing the foam in the tubes. *(2)*

ii) Suggest how the students could have measured the height of the foam. *(2)*

b) i) Two students suggested drawing a graph to display the results. Make a drawing to show the axes they would have used for their graph. Include the scale and label for each axis. (Do not plot any results.) *(3)*

ii) Another student was not happy with the results and said they should do the investigation again. Suggest reasons why this student was not happy with the results. *(2)*

iii) Outline **two** ways that the method used in the experiment could be improved and in each case give a reason for the suggested improvement. *(2)*

c) Write down a conclusion the students could make from their results in this experiment. *(2)*

(Total = 13 marks)

Student 1 response Total 3/13	Marker comments and tips for success
a) i) *The heat is driving the dissolved gases out of the solution as bubbles of gas, which are making the foam.* O	Student 1 has not said that the gas is carbon dioxide or linked this with respiration.
ii) *They could use a tape measure* ✔	A tape measure is acceptable as a scale to make the measurement but no description given of how it would be used.
b) i) *Student 1 graph shows axes with height as the vertical axis and temperature on the horizontal axis, but neither axes is labelled. Axis correct way round* ✔*, labelling* O	Student 1 gains 1 mark for showing the axes correctly but no further marks as the axes are not labelled.
ii) *The results in the two tubes should be exactly the same.* O	This is not enough to gain a mark. In an experiment, the tubes would not necessarily be exactly the same.
iii) *Use a more accurate clock for measuring the 30 minutes, so that the timing errors will be less.* O *Use a stronger sugar solution so more foam is produced more quickly, for measuring.* ✔	The tubes are all removed from their water baths at the same time, so the accuracy of the clock is not relevant. The suggestion of using a stronger sugar solution linked to producing more foam is something that could help so gains a mark under 'eq'.
c) *Increases in temperature cause gas bubbles in foam to expand more.* O	Although student 1 has noted that increase in temperature affects the gas bubbles, there is no reference to the effect of temperature on respiration. In giving a conclusion, it is important to link the results to the original intention in carrying out the investigation and show what has been found out.

Student 2 response Total 11/13	Marker comments and tips for success
a) i) *The yeast are respiring ✔ the sugar in the water, producing carbon dioxide ✔ bubbles as waste, which are forming the foam.*	Student 2 correctly identified the bubbles of gas as carbon dioxide and linked these with respiration.
ii) *They could place a ruler ✔ against the side of the tube and hold it level with their eye to judge the distance from the liquid surface to the top of the foam. ✔*	Student 2 gave a detailed description of how to measure the height of the foam and gains both marks.
b) i) *Student 2 graph shows axes with height as the vertical axis and temperature on the horizontal axis. Student 2 gives no unit for height but gives °C for the temperature axis. Axes correct way round ✔, labelling ✔*	Student 2's graph shows the axes correctly and gives a full label (with unit) for the temperature, so gains 2 marks, but did not give the unit for the height so missed the third mark.
ii) *More sets of results would have improved the reliability of the data, ✔ and anomalous results would have less of an effect. ✔*	Student 2 notes that there is an anomalous result so gains 1 mark for understanding the effect of anomalous results. The comment on reliability is sensible, and implies the candidate is 'not happy' because there is only one set of results (and with more it would be more reliable).
iii) *Collect the bubbles of gas so that the volume can be measured properly. O Repeat the experiment several more times ✔, so that a mean can be calculated. ✔*	Student 2 sees the need to collect the volume of gas but gives no description of how this would be done. Repeat and calculate a mean both get a mark. Reference to reliability was given in ii), but there is enough in iii) for student 2 to gain 2 marks.
c) *Increasing temperature up to 50 °C causes increased rate of respiration in yeast, ✔ but after this temperature enzyme denaturation occurs, and the rate falls. ✔*	Student 2 makes two correct statements that are acceptable for the conclusion to the investigation (looking at the effect of temperature on respiration in yeast).

Practice questions

2 A grower in England had a farm where she grew vegetables. She grew some inside a polytunnel and some outside in a field. She sold the vegetables direct to local shops and markets.

The figures in the list on the right show the yields she obtained with French beans in 2011. Inside the polytunnels the beans were grown in rows, with a total length of 40 m. Outside in the field they were grown in rows with a total length of 100 m. She picked the beans when they were ready and weighed them to find the mass in kg each time she harvested them.

a) i) Draw a suitable table that you can use to present the data so that you can compare the total yield of the beans inside the polytunnel and outside in the field. Then organise the data in your table. *(4)*

ii) Calculate the total yield of beans harvested from each place on the farm. *(2)*

b) i) The total yield of beans from inside the polytunnel is 1.36 kg per metre of row. Calculate the total yield of beans grown outside in the field in kg per metre of row. *(1)*

ii) Suggest reasons for the difference in yield of beans in the polytunnel compared with the field. *(2)*

c) The grower sowed the bean seeds in trays then planted out the young plants when they had germinated and grown to a suitable size. The table on the next page shows the dates on which she sowed the seeds and when she planted them out.

Mass of beans harvested in kg (dates of harvest are given in brackets)

June (inside)
0.85 (10th); 0.75 (11th); 0.8 (13th); 1.6 (17th); 4.6 (19th); 1.2 (21st); 2.1 (23rd); 2.2 (24th); 4.8 (27th); 3.1 (28th); 1.4 (29th)

July (inside)
5.3 (3rd); 5.8 (6th); 2.0 (11th); 1.6 (13th); 1.0 (14th); 1.6 (16th); 0.75 (31st)

July (outside)
3.5 (10th); 2.0 (11th); 1.6 (21st); 2.0 (23rd); 1.0 (27th); 0.6 (31st)

August (inside)
2.2 (5th); 0.75 (7th); 2.0 (11th); 1.5 (14th); 1.8 (17th); 1.8 (20th); 2.0 (23rd); 0.8 (28th)

August (outside)
3.2 (3rd); 2.4 (5th); 1.5 (7th); 4.5 (9th); 4.4 (14th); 1.1 (17th); 1.0 (25th); 0.5 (28th)

September (outside)
0.8 (5th); 0.6 (8th); 0.6 (14th)

Place on farm	Sowed bean seeds	Planted out seedlings	Harvest period	
			start	finish
Inside polytunnel	22 March 8 April	16 to 20 April		
Outside in field	18 April 16 May	11 May 14 May 11 June		

In the spaces in the table, write in the dates for the start and finish of the harvest periods for the beans grown in both places. *(2)*

d) Use information provided as well as your own calculations to answer these questions.

i) Suggest **two** advantages for the grower of growing the beans in the polytunnel. *(2)*

ii) Suggest **one** way that the grower benefits from growing the beans both inside the polytunnel and outside in the field. *(1)*

(Total = 14 marks)

3 The steps shown in the diagram summarise a procedure that can be used in a school or college laboratory to clone cauliflowers (a vegetable). It illustrates the essential stages of micropropagation techniques used in commercial laboratories, where it is carried out under carefully controlled sterile conditions.

SDICN is a sterilising solution, similar to that used for sterilising babies' bottles and for small amounts of drinking water.

Agar is a jelly that has been specially prepared and poured into the glass tubes, under sterile conditions. The agar contains SDICN, sugars, mineral ions and kinetin (a plant growth regulator).

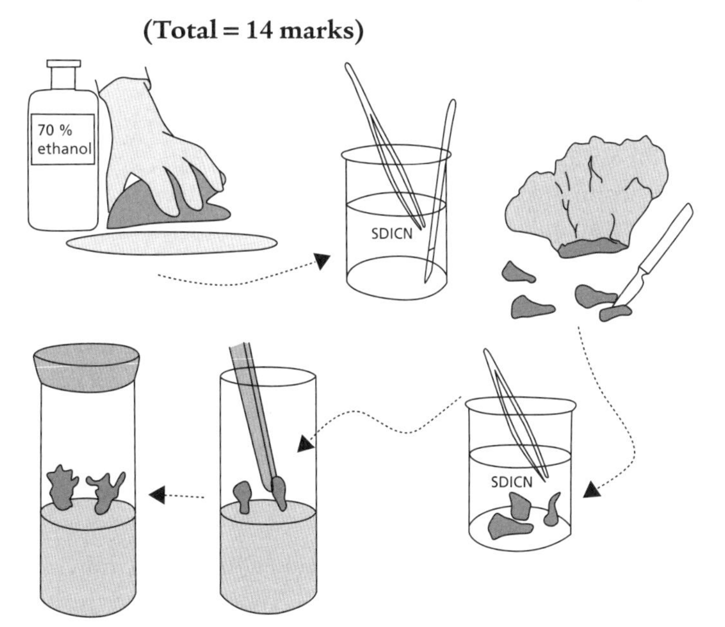

Step 1: clean bench with alcohol and paper towel.
Step 2: dip forceps and scalpel (knife) in beaker containing sterilising solution.
Step 3: use scalpel to cut a small 'floret' from the head (white part) of a cauliflower and place it on the lid of a sterile Petri dish.
Step 4: cut this floret lengthwise into several smaller pieces, about 3 to 5 mm long.
Step 5: use forceps and transfer these smaller pieces into a tube containing SDICN. Leave them in the SDICN for 15 minutes. Shake the tube gently for 5 seconds in each minute.
Step 6: use forceps and transfer the small pieces into separate tubes containing the agar. Press the stalk into the agar. Replace the lid on each tube.
Step 7: place the tubes in a warm place (say about 35 °C) and in the light.
Finally: After about 10 days the small pieces should begin to look green and show some growth. Later roots and shoots begin to develop.

a) i) List **three** steps when the sterile solution (SDICN) is used. *(1)*

ii) Explain why it is necessary to use sterile conditions. *(2)*

b) i) In micropropagation techniques, what name is given to the 'smaller pieces' cut from the cauliflower? *(1)*

ii) Why are sugars included in the agar in the tubes? *(1)*

iii) Explain why the tubes are left in the light. *(2)*

c) The method described is similar to one used by research organisations interested in the conservation of rare and endangered plants. A scientist working in remote places can take the equipment into the field. Without damaging the plant, the scientist can follow the procedure and remove small parts of the endangered plants, getting them into the tubes as described for step 6. The scientists then take the tubes back to their laboratory to allow them to grow into whole plants.

i) Suggest why scientists wish to conserve rare and endangered species of plants. *(2)*

ii) Explain why micropropagation techniques are useful in this conservation work. *(2)*

iii) Suggest the advantages for the scientists of using the method and equipment described and collecting their small pieces of plants for micropropagation in the field. *(2)*

(Total = 13 marks)

4 Some students carried out an investigation into the effect of fertiliser on the growth of grass seedlings.

They grew the grass in small compartments in a seed tray, as shown in the diagram. Each of the trays had 10 compartments and they gave the same treatment to all the compartments of a tray. Each day the students checked that there was enough water in the tray and added more if needed. The sand contains no nutrients.

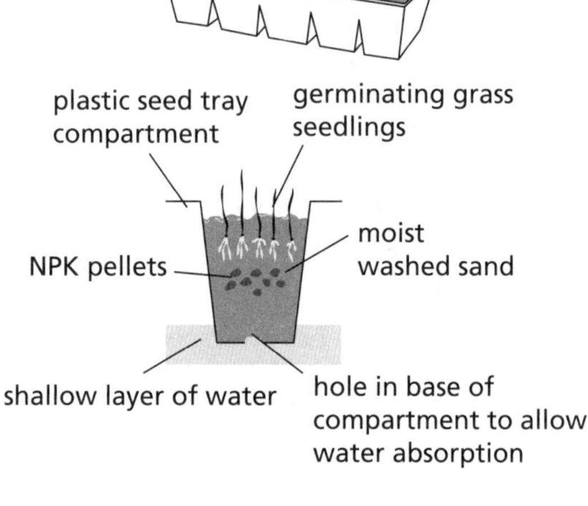

The students added the fertiliser as 'NPK' pellets. NPK indicates that the pellets contain nitrogen, phosphorus and potassium. The pellets release the fertiliser slowly, so that the supply is continuous throughout the investigation. The number of pellets added for each tray is shown in the table. They added 10 grass seeds to each compartment.

After 2 weeks, they measured the height of each individual grass seedling in all the compartments. They measured the height from the top of the sand in the seed tray to the highest leaf tip of the grass. They calculated the mean height for each treatment (number of pellets). Their results are shown in the table.

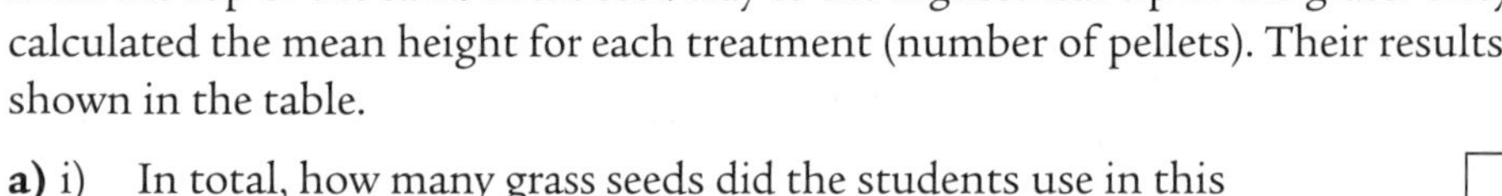

In each compartment	
Number of NPK pellets	**Mean height of seedlings in mm**
0	75
5	165
10	180
20	156
30	60

a) i) In total, how many grass seeds did the students use in this investigation? Show how you work out your answer. *(2)*

ii) Suggest why the students decided to use this number of seeds. *(1)*

iii) Suggest why the students calculated the mean of their individual measurements. *(2)*

b) Plot a line graph on a grid of graph paper 10 cm high by 8 cm wide to show how fertiliser affected the growth of the grass seedlings in this investigation. Use a ruler to join the points with straight lines. *(5)*

c) i) Give **two** factors that the students should have kept constant for all seedlings when doing this investigation. *(2)*

ii) Give **two** possible sources of error in the way the students carried out this investigation. *(2)*

d) Using the results of this experiment, what advice would you give to a farmer wishing to use fertiliser on the crops being grown on a farm? *(2)*

(Total = 16 marks)

Understanding structure, function and processes

Example

1 Peter is a fruit farmer. He wants to improve the variety of strawberries grown on his farm so that he can use them for production of strawberry juice. He wrote down some ideas to help him plan what to do.

The statements A to G are the ideas for his plan for the selective breeding programme, but he realised that the statements are not in the correct sequence.

Statements

A select a variety of strawberry that produces fruits with a lot of juice – call this a 'juicy' strawberry
B transfer pollen from the flower on one juicy strawberry plant to the stigma of a flower on another juicy strawberry plant ('pollination by hand')
C when the strawberry plants are beginning to flower (on a juicy strawberry plant), before they open, enclose the flowers in a thin, pollen-proof cloth bag
D grow the seeds ('pips') from the juiciest strawberry fruits and wait for two years for the plants to produce flowers and strawberry fruits again
E collect the strawberry fruits from the strawberry plants that are pollinated by hand and check that they are juicy
F select the juiciest strawberry fruits from the plants that are pollinated by hand
G repeat the process for several generations (for at least 10 years) and each year select the juiciest strawberries to be the parents for the next generation

a) Arrange these stages in the correct sequence to make a sensible plan for the selective breeding programme. Write your answers in a table. Stage A is the first, but the rest are out of order. *(3)*

b) i) Peter planned to pollinate the flowers by hand. Suggest how pollination usually occurs in strawberry flowers. *(1)*

ii) Explain why Peter wanted to put thin pollen-proof cloth bags over the flowers before pollinating them. *(2)*

c) Peter saw that it would take many years to develop an improved variety of juicy strawberry plants using selective breeding techniques.

Name **two** techniques he could use immediately to grow more strawberry plants that are genetically the same as the juicy ones he had selected. *(2)*

(Total = 8 marks)

Student 1 response Total 2/8	Marker comments and tips for success
a) A F D G ✓✓	The sequence is incomplete, but student 1 gains 2 marks for two correct pairs: F before D and D before G. The 'statements' tell the complete story, so in a question of this sort you should read them all carefully to help you work out your response, in a situation that is likely to be unfamiliar to you.
b) i) Pollen swims from the stamen to the ovule. O	Even though student 1 understands that pollen has to reach the ovule, 'swims' is incorrect so gains no marks.
ii) So that he can label the flowers clearly and stop pollen escaping. O	Student 1 misses the important step that pollen is brought from the (selected) juicy strawberry plant.
c) He could ask the genetic engineer to copy the juicy flowers exactly. O	Student 1's answer gives no suggestion of asexual reproduction – either by runners or by plant tissue culture – so gains no marks.

Student 2 response Total 5/8	Marker comments and tips for success
a) B E C F D G ✔✔	The sequence is nearly correct but C is misplaced, so student 2 cannot get full marks, but gains 2 marks for two correct pairs: B before E and F before D.
b) i) Pollen is carried from the anther of a flower to the stigma of another flower by the body of an insect. ✔	Reference to 'insect' is correct for 1 mark.
ii) To prevent pollination of the flower by insects or wind before he gets to do it by hand. ✔	Student 2's answer says enough to give the idea of keeping out insects.
c) He could ask a gardener to take cuttings ✔ from the stem of the juicy plant, as well as encouraging the plant to grow more runners.	A 'cutting' is a reasonable suggestion as a means of asexual reproduction. 'Runners' are also correct for strawberries (and you should be familiar with this as an example of asexual reproduction for strawberries), but student 2 had already gained the mark for 'asexual' reproduction, so scores 1 mark overall.

Practice questions

2 Some people who have diabetes can control it by having injections of insulin. It is now possible to produce insulin from bacteria that have been genetically modified (GM bacteria) to produce human insulin. Scientists have genetically modified *E. coli* bacteria so that they contain the gene for human insulin.

The diagram shows a fermenter that can be used for large-scale production of insulin from GM bacteria.

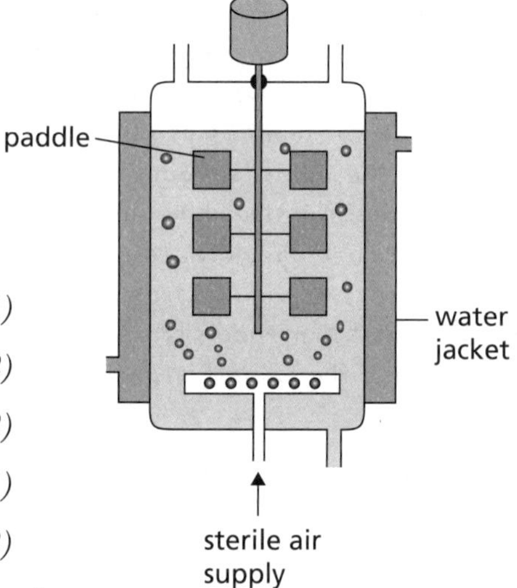

a) i) On the diagram, label the outlet from the water jacket. *(1)*

ii) Explain why the water jacket is necessary. *(2)*

b) i) Explain why the paddle is used in the fermenter vessel. *(2)*

ii) Suggest why the pH control is included. *(1)*

iii) State why a sterile air supply is provided for the fermenter vessel. *(2)*

iv) Suggest **two** nutrients that would be included for the bacteria growing in the vessel and state why each is required. *(2)*

c) i) Name the enzyme that would be used to cut the insulin gene from human DNA. *(1)*

ii) Before scientists had developed the technique of inserting the insulin gene into bacteria, insulin was often extracted from the pancreas of pigs and used to treat diabetes. Suggest why people prefer to use human insulin from GM bacteria rather than from pigs. *(2)*

(Total = 13 marks)

3 When tomatoes ripen, they turn red, become sweeter and other flavours develop making them good to eat. At the same time, material between the cell walls begins to go soft. An enzyme called PG controls this reaction.

Growers often pick their tomatoes before they are ripe because they have not yet started to go soft. This means that they are less likely to get damaged when they are transported to shops and markets where they are sold. However, often the flavour of tomatoes is not so good before they are fully ripe.

Scientists have produced a genetically modified (GM) tomato in which the PG enzyme is much less active than in the normal tomato. This means the growers pick the tomatoes when they are ripe and taste better, but they do not go soft so quickly. This reduces losses after harvest from spoiled tomato fruits.

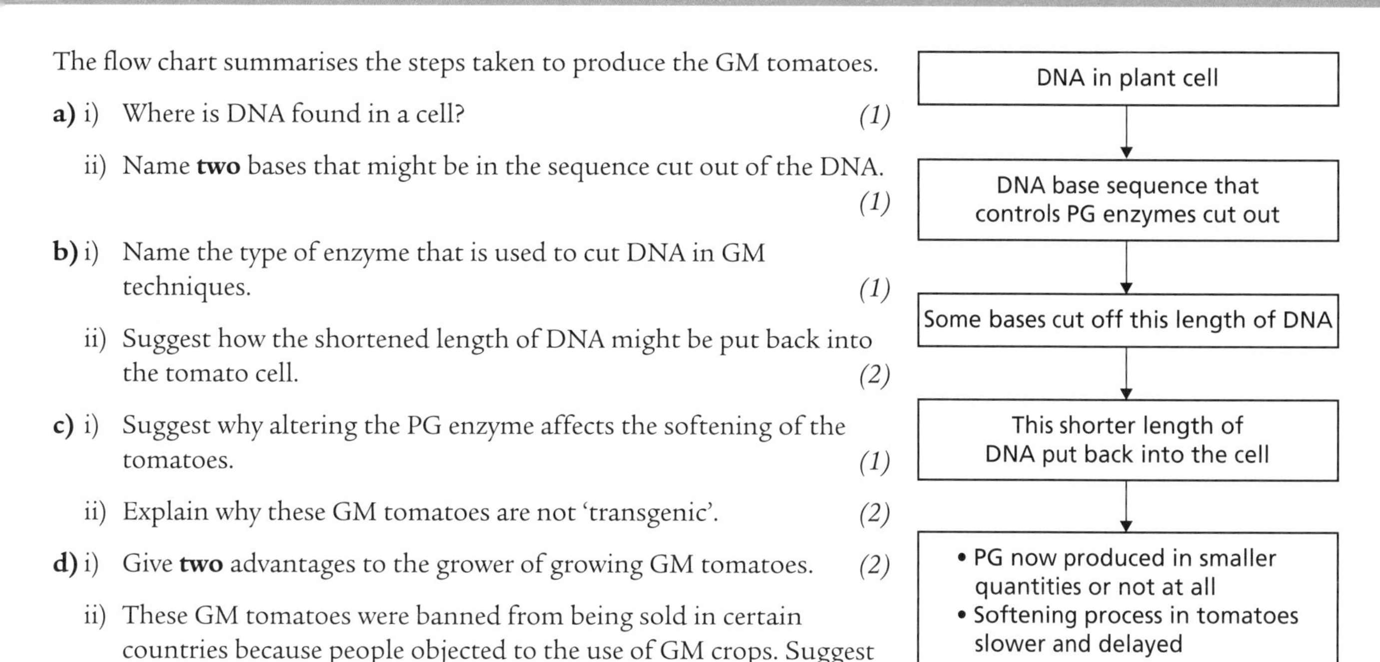

The flow chart summarises the steps taken to produce the GM tomatoes.

a) i) Where is DNA found in a cell? *(1)*

ii) Name **two** bases that might be in the sequence cut out of the DNA. *(1)*

b) i) Name the type of enzyme that is used to cut DNA in GM techniques. *(1)*

ii) Suggest how the shortened length of DNA might be put back into the tomato cell. *(2)*

c) i) Suggest why altering the PG enzyme affects the softening of the tomatoes. *(1)*

ii) Explain why these GM tomatoes are not 'transgenic'. *(2)*

d) i) Give **two** advantages to the grower of growing GM tomatoes. *(2)*

ii) These GM tomatoes were banned from being sold in certain countries because people objected to the use of GM crops. Suggest **one** reason why some people object to GM crops. *(1)*

(Total = 11 marks)

4 Scientists have developed techniques that they can use to clone mammals. Dolly (a sheep) was an early example of a successful cloned mammal. Dolly was born in 1996. Several other mammals have now been cloned, including a dog (Snuppy), a cat (Copy Cat), a gaur (an endangered species, related to cattle), a camel and a goat.

The statements A to G describe stages in the technique used for cloning, but the statements are not in the correct sequence.

Statements

A skin cells are taken from the original animal to be cloned
B the embryo develops into a fetus and is born
C the embryo grows on an artificial medium
D the egg cell containing the skin cell nucleus develops into an embryo
E the nucleus is removed from an egg cell so that this becomes an enucleated cell
F the embryo is implanted into a surrogate mother
G the skin cell nucleus is inserted into the egg cell

a) Arrange these stages in the correct sequence and write your answers in a table. For each stage, state whether the cell(s) are haploid, diploid or have no nucleus (no chromosomes). Stage A is the first, but the rest are out of order. *(5)*

b) Give **two** ways in which sexual reproduction in mammals differs from the processes used for production of offspring in cloning techniques used with mammals. *(2)*

c) Suggest **two** reasons why cloning of mammals may be undertaken. *(2)*

(Total = 9 marks)

Extended writing

Example

1 Describe how a fish farmer produces large numbers of healthy fish for sale from a freshwater fish farm. *(6)*

Student 1 response
The fish farmer buys small fish from a supplier, and grows them up in his fish farm, so he can sell them at a profit. To help them grow quickly he adds lots of fish food to the water. He also adds extra oxygen because the fish need to breathe. The fish are crowded together so he has to check that they are healthy, otherwise people might not want to buy them.
Student 2 response
The farmer needs to sell fish all year round, so he buys new fish in batches. Each batch is kept in a different container, and is fed protein-rich food in order to speed their growth. The oxygen consumed by the respiration of the fish must be replaced, and this is achieved by pumping bubbles of air and using paddles to stir the water. The wastes produced by the fish must be removed, and if any diseased fish are spotted, they must be removed before all the fish become infected.
Mark scheme
The mark scheme shows how marks are awarded. (1) fish contained in pond / tank / cage in water / eq (2) water kept oxygenated by paddles / aerators / sprinklers / recirculated / eq (3) net / eq covers container / eq to prevent predation / interspecific competition / eq (4) prevent overcrowding / watch fish density / separate into other tanks / eq (5) separate fish of different sizes / large ones become aggressive / ref intraspecific competition / eq (6) regular feeding in small amounts / appropriate food / e.g. high protein especially in younger stages / eq (7) removal waste nitrogenous material / excreta / eq / prevent pollution / eq (8) check for disease and remove unhealthy fish / use antibiotics in food / eq (9) select good breeding stock / eq (10) containers / eq with fish of different ages to allow continuity of supply / eq (11+) *accept other points relating to water quality (e.g. ref temperature, pH) + quality of fish stock + detail of fish feed (e.g. canthoxanthin for flesh colour)* Total: 6

Student 1 response Total 1/6	Marker comments and tips for success
The fish farmer buys small fish from a supplier, and grows them up in his fish farm, so he can sell them at a profit. O	Student 1 has not said enough here to gain any of the marks.
To help them grow quickly he adds lots of fish food to the water. O	To gain mark (6), student 1 needs to give more detail about how much food, when to feed or refer to high protein.
He also adds extra oxygen because the fish need to breathe. O	To gain mark (2), student 1 needs to describe how the water is kept oxygenated, by referring to paddles, aerators or other points listed.
The fish are crowded together so he has to check that they are healthy, ✔ otherwise people might not want to buy them.	Student 1 does not gain mark (4) because there is no mention of preventing overcrowding. However, student 1 just says enough to gain mark (8), referring to checking and removing unhealthy fish.

Student 2 response Total 5/6	Marker comments and tips for success
The farmer needs to sell fish all year round, so he buys new fish in batches. Each batch is kept in a different container, ✔	This is a suitable description for 'continuity of supply' and gains mark (10). There is no description of the container so student 2 does not gain mark (1).
and is fed protein-rich food ✔ in order to speed their growth.	Student 2 gains mark (6) with this reference to feeding.
The oxygen consumed by the respiration of the fish must be replaced, and this is achieved by pumping bubbles of air ✔ and using paddles to stir the water.	Student 2 gains mark (2) – 'pumping bubbles of air' is accepted for aerators and 'using paddles to stir' is another way of getting the same mark.

(continued)

Student 2 response Total 5/6	Marker comments and tips for success
The waste produced by the fish must be removed, ✔	Even though student 2 did not say 'nitrogenous' material, saying 'produced by the fish' gives enough to gain mark (7).
and if any diseased fish are spotted, they must be removed ✔ *before all the fish become infected.*	Student 2 gains mark (8).

Extended writing questions – general advice

The list below summarises the skills being tested and how to approach your answers to this type of question. You should read this advice and also look at the mark scheme for the particular question you are doing, together with the guidance for students to help you understand the mark scheme.

- Skills being tested include the ability to select and organise information.
- Facts must be correct and relevant to the question.
- Often a single word is not enough for a mark but requires further description or elaboration in some way. For example, in this question on fish farming, student 2 has not given any description of the container, so does not gain mark (1).
- The question may expect you to make links between different aspects of a topic, so make sure those links are clear in what you write.
- The question may refer to two different parts of a topic – say features or processes to compare. Make sure you cover both aspects, or you will not be able to gain full marks.
- No marks are awarded for the quality of written work (such as spelling, grammar and organisation of subject matter), but you are more likely to include all the relevant material if you organise it sensibly and logically. It is also easier for the examiner to read if your handwriting is legible and written in sentences that are clearly set out.
- Sometimes you may decide that it is useful to draw a diagram to help with your answer. If you do this, make sure the diagram is labelled or annotated with notes so that it can be understood and makes links with the rest of your written answer.
- The mark allocation is usually 6 marks. This gives a guide as to how long you spend on this question in relation to the rest of the paper (probably about 6 minutes). Use your time sensibly by writing down a brief plan or a list of what you want to include, as this will help you select and organise the material better and gain more marks for your answer. If you have 6 minutes, you can spend about 3 minutes planning and deciding what you are going to write. Then 3 minutes is enough to write an answer that gains full marks.

Practice questions

2 Explain how glasshouses and polytunnels can be used to grow crops, such as tomatoes or peppers, in a way that the grower benefits from increased yields. *(6)*

3 Explain how microorganisms are beneficial to the lives of people. Include suitable examples to illustrate your answer. *(6)*

4 Explain how artificial selection differs from natural selection as a way of changing characteristics of populations of plants and animals. Include examples to illustrate your answer. *(6)*

Experimental design (CORMS)

Example

1 When bananas ripen, their skin turns from green (for unripe bananas) through a series of colours to yellow (for ripe bananas). For fruits, a gas called ethene helps with the ripening process. Ripe fruits give off ethene.

Design an investigation to find out if placing a ripe tomato with green bananas speeds up their ripening. *(6)*

Student response
CORMS: Outline: Put green bananas into bags – some with a ripe tomato. Record time for the bananas to go yellow. O: I would use bananas from the same bunch, so they were the same variety, the same size and the same colour green (so the same ripeness). The tomatoes must also be as similar as possible. C: Put the bananas into identical polybags, transparent, to show the colour of the bananas clearly. Five bags would contain one banana and five would have one banana and one tomato. The bags would be sealed with a double knot to make sure no gas escaped. R: I would observe 5 sets of bags to make sure my results were reliable. S: I would keep the bags in a dark cupboard, where the temperature was the same for all the bags. M: I would check the bags twice a day, recording the date and time, and the colour of each banana. I would use a photograph of a ripe banana to check the final yellow colour. I would record the time, in hours, for each banana to become yellow and compare the results.
Mark scheme
(1) C – bananas in container with and without tomato (2) O – same variety of banana / same stage of ripeness / same colour at start / eq (3) R – repeats with several bananas / several batches bananas / eq (4) M1 – measure colour of banana (e. g. match on colour scale) / eq (5) M2 – time stated to reach this colour (6) S1 – same container around same number of bananas + tomato / eq (7) S2 – same temperature / same light / same humidity / same other variable / eq Total = 6

The mark scheme shows how marks are awarded. The meaning of the letters C, O, R, M, S is expalained on the next page.

Student response Total 6/6	Marker comments and tips for success
CORMS	Always start your answer by writing down the word 'CORMS'. This will remind you to check that your answer covers all relevant aspects. Another good idea is to write these letters next to the descriptions so you can check that your answer is complete.
Outline: Put green bananas into bags – some with a ripe tomato. Record time for the bananas to go yellow.	Planning the method in outline before you write the answer will help you when you write in more detail about each part.
O: I would use bananas from the same bunch, so they were the same variety ✔ (O), the same size and the same colour green (so the same ripeness). The tomatoes must also be as similar as possible.	A good answer, listing several aspects that need to be kept constant in order for the comparison to be fair. Do not worry about losing marks if you get the CORMS letters wrong – the examiner only marks the written text.

(continued)

Student response Total 6/6	Marker comments and tips for success
C: Put the bananas into identical polybags, ✔ (S1) transparent, to show the colour of the bananas clearly. Five bags would contain one banana and five ✔ (R) would have one banana and one tomato ✔ (C). The bags would be sealed with a double knot to make sure no gas escaped.	A good, concise answer. Mark S1 awarded for the use of identical polythene bags with the same numbers of bananas in them. Mark R awarded for mentioning the need for repeats (5 of each bag). Mark C awarded for explaining that the control is a bag with just a banana in it, while the test bags contain a banana and a tomato. Note that although the student put all of this under 'C', the examiner awarded marks as appropriate.
R: I would observe 5 sets of bags to make sure my results were reliable.	The R mark was allocated in the previous paragraph.
S: I would keep the bags in a dark cupboard, ✔ (S2) where the temperature was the same for all the bags.	Mark S1 awarded for keeping all bags in the dark (i.e. light kept the same) but could also have been awarded for keeping the temperature the same.
M: I would check the bags twice a day, recording the date and time, and the colour of each banana. I would use a photograph of a ripe banana to check the final yellow colour ✔ (M1). I would record the time, in hours, ✔ (M2) for each banana to become yellow and compare the results.	Student gave sufficient detail for assessing the final yellow colour, so mark M1 awarded. Sufficient detail given for measuring the time, M2, (daily checks and suitable unit of time – hours) but maximum of 6 marks already reached.

Experimental design questions – general advice

These are the 'experimental design' questions, now often known as the 'CORMS' questions. If we look a little further at this name, we see how it helps provide a framework for your answer. The letters are given in the mark scheme and it helps you to use them in your answers. In this way you can check that you have included reference to all the necessary factors that should be considered in designing the investigation or experiment asked for in the question.

We now look at each letter in turn.

C = what is being **C**hanged (or **C**ompared) in the experiment. This is the independent variable and also covers the idea of a **C**ontrol. In this question on bananas ripening, the change is the presence (or not) of ethene from the ripe tomato.
O = the **O**rganism being used and some statement about it to make sure the investigation is valid. Often this is covered by reference to using the same species or variety so that the effect of the change can be judged fairly. So, in this question, all bananas should be of the same variety or from the same batch and starting from the same stage of ripeness.
R = **R**eplication or repeats, so that several results are obtained rather than relying on a single measurement or observation. This is good practice in any experimental work.
M1 + **M2** = the **M**easurements taken. This is the dependent variable, because it 'depends' on what the change is when setting up the experiment. Often this may refer to a change in mass, or height or something you can measure in numbers. For the question on bananas, you decide on an 'end-point' on the colour scale (which represents the stage of ripeness). A second M mark is usually given for reference to a time scale – in this case, how long it takes the banana to reach the colour chosen for the end-point. It is important to suggest an actual time – this shows you are thinking about whether the change occurs in seconds, or hours or perhaps weeks. You may not know the correct time, but make a sensible attempt. In the group of Practice questions below, the cabbages treated with fertiliser are likely to take several weeks before reaching a stage to be weighed, whereas the yoghurt investigation is likely to be completed in a few hours.
S1 + **S2** = a variable that must be kept the **S**ame or controlled in this experiment. Such factors may include the quantity used (same volume, same mass) or other variables such as same temperature, same humidity or whatever is appropriate for the investigation. Usually there are plenty of factors you could choose, but make sure it is relevant to the investigation.

Lastly – the topic in the question may be a novel one – so perhaps not something you have already studied in your specification, but you should be able to apply and adapt these principles to any of the questions set. Spend a couple of minutes thinking how you would plan the investigation, then try to follow through the CORMS letters to make sure you cover all essential aspects of the design.

Practice questions

2 A group of farmers grew cabbages in their fields. They wanted to increase the yield of their crop and one farmer suggested they use fertiliser.

Design an investigation to find out if using animal manure as the fertiliser increases the yield of the cabbages. *(6)*

3 When yoghurt is made, fruit is sometimes added. This fruit can be included at the start of the fermentation or after incubation is complete.

Design an investigation to find out if adding fruit (such as peaches) at the start of the process affects the time it takes for the yoghurt to set. *(6)*

4 A group of students stood in pairs in a circle on a games field. A teacher in the middle blew a whistle. When the whistle blew one student in the pair started to run up and down on the spot. The other student in the pair had a stopwatch and noted how quickly the partner responded to the sound of the whistle.

Design an investigation to find out if reaction times are different if the student is blindfolded (e.g. wearing a dark bag over the head). *(6)*

Index